Creating Melodies

Stefan Hollos and J. Richard Hollos

Creating Melodies
by Stefan Hollos and J. Richard Hollos

Copyright ©2018 by Exstrom Laboratories LLC

Abrazol Publishing
an imprint of Exstrom Laboratories LLC
662 Nelson Park Drive, Longmont, CO 80503-7674 U.S.A.

Publisher's Cataloging in Publication Data
Hollos, Stefan
Creating Melodies / by Stefan Hollos and J. Richard Hollos
p. cm.
Includes bibliographical references.
Paper ISBN: 978-1-887187-36-7
Ebook ISBN: 978-1-887187-37-4
Library of Congress Control Number: 2018909678

1. Computer composition (Music) 2. Music–Melodic analysis
I. Title. II. Hollos, Stefan.
MT56.H65 2018
781.4 HOL

Contents

INTRODUCTION

This book is about creating melodies. For our purposes, a melody is defined simply as a sequence of notes or chords. When we use the word **note** it may refer to a single note or a chord, i.e. multiple notes played simultaneously. An important part of a melody is the rhythm which we define as the length of each note in the sequence. A given sequence of notes can be played with many different rhythms. Rhythms have a significant effect on the perception of the melody. We will discuss rhythms but will not be concerned so much with the question of generating them which we covered in our previous book: *Creating Rhythms*.

So to create melodies you need two things: a set of notes and a rhythm. The question is, given a set of notes how do you form an interesting sequence, i.e. a melody? If you chose each note in the sequence at random the result is not likely to be interesting. The same is true if the sequence is too simple and repetitive. The interesting sequences lie somewhere between the completely random and the totally repetitive. How do you find them?

The obvious thing to do is to use rules for selecting each subsequent note in a sequence. We will show how to set up these rules. There are many ways to do it, ranging from formal language theory methods to the

1

strictly mathematical. Don't let this scare you. We will present these methods in simple easy to understand terms that we hope everyone will be able to understand and use regardless of background. There will be some mathematics for those interested in that sort of thing but it is not essential.

Much of what we will do in this book comes from the theory of formal languages. In particular, we will generate sequences using a simple computational device called an automaton. This amounts to defining a set of sequences as a regular language and it will allow us to explore a large space of potentially interesting melodies.

A regular language can always be defined in terms of an automaton which is simply a set of states and rules for moving between the states. The automaton has an intuitive pictorial representation that makes it easy to understand. After reading this book anyone should be able to create their own automaton to generate their own unique melodies.

A regular language is the simplest type of formal language. Moving up in the hierarchy we come to languages defined in terms of something called a context free grammar. In most cases these can be represented by an automaton with an infinite number of states and closely approximated by an automaton with a large but finite number of states. We will not specifically discuss context free grammars in this book but we will give some examples of automata with large numbers of states.

Anyone interested in context free grammars should look at our book: *Finite Automata and Regular Expressions: Problems and Solutions.* At the end of that book we give some examples of how to go from an infinite state automaton to a context free grammar. It is perhaps the easiest introduction to context free grammars and may spark some ideas on how to extend the methods used in this book.

One of the problems with a regular language or a context free grammar is that the number of melodies contained in the language is usually very large, in some cases it can be in the millions or billions. You can't possibly listen to all of them. The thing to do then is to sample from the set. We will show a couple of ways to do that. One way is to use a probabilistic automaton.

With a probabilistic automaton we can create melodies that emulate the style of a certain composer or genre of music. We do this by extracting statistics of note or chord progressions from a set of compositions representative of the composer or genre. We can then create an automaton that generates sequences with those same statistics. We will show an example of how this is done for the nineteenth century American composer Stephen

Foster.

Another way to generate melodies is by taking walks on a lattice. Each point on the lattice represents a note or chord, and you create a melody by starting at one point and continually hopping to a neighboring point until you reach some end point. A good model for such a lattice is the set of bass buttons on an accordion, or the fret board of a guitar. We will show how to do this with some software that comes with the book.

Finally we will discuss a more mathematical method for generating sequences. These sequences are called de Bruijn sequences. For those of you who have read our rhythms book, you will recall that we used them to create rhythms. It turns out they are also good for creating melodies. You do not need to understand the mathematics behind these sequences just to use them, but we will present some of it for those interested.

This book comes with a lot of software that you can download from the book's website at:

http://www.abrazol.com/books/melody1/

All of the software is documented in the software chapter. It is written in ANSI C code and should compile with any C compiler. It is also platform independent and should work on Linux, macOS, or Windows. You do not need to understand C code to use the programs. They are run on the command line with input parameters and files that are documented in the book.

You can listen to all the melodies in this book at the book's website. They are in both MIDI and MP3 format.

Besides the software on the book's website, other software you'll need to get the most out of the book is:

- An ANSI C compiler like **gcc**, available at http://gcc.gnu.org/

- `abc2midi` program. The `abc2midi` program is part of a package called `abcMIDI` that can be downloaded from
  https://ifdo.ca/~seymour/runabc/top.html
  or
  https://sourceforge.net/projects/abc/

- A MIDI player like `TiMidity++` available at https://sourceforge.net/projects/timidity/

In addition to the software, it's helpful to know a little bit of music theory, but most of what you need is in the Notes and Chords section near the end of this book. To go deeper, a nice book is *Barron's AP Music Theory* by Nancy Scoggin (2010).

We had a lot of fun writing this book. In fact it took us so long to write it because it was hard to tear ourselves away from creating so much interesting new music and write up the results. Now it's your turn to have some fun.

So let's get started.

AUTOMATA

One way to generate all melodies that conform to a certain pattern is with an automaton. An automaton consists of a set of states and a set of transitions between the states. A state usually only allows transitions to a subset of all the states. One of the states is designated as the start state and a subset of the states is designated as possible end states.

Each transition from one state to another has an output associated with it and these outputs are used to generate strings. The set of all the strings an automaton can generate is called a regular language. For a more in depth discussion of automata and regular languages see our book *Finite Automata and Regular Expressions*.

To generate an output string of length n you begin at the start state and follow one of its transitions to another state. The output associated with that transition forms the beginning of the string. Now you follow one of the transitions from the new state to the next state. The output of that transition gets added to the output string. You continue the process for n transitions. If the last state is one of the end states then the output string belongs to the regular language of the automaton.

This is best illustrated with a simple example. The

automaton in figure 1 has only two states labeled 0
and 1. The 0 state has two transitions. One transition
is back to itself on which it outputs a 0. The other
transition is to state 1 on which it outputs a 1. State
1 has only one transition back to state 0 on which it
outputs a 0.

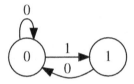

Figure 1: Automaton for strings of 0's and 1's with no
repeats of two or more 1's in a row.

If we make 0 the starting state and allow 0 or 1 to be an
ending state can you guess what kind of output strings
will be generated? It should be be clear from the description that each output string will be composed of
0's and 1's with no repeats of two or more 1's in a row.
All 21 such strings of length 6 are shown below.

000000 000001 000010 000100 000101 001000
001001 001010 010000 010001 010010 010100
010101 100000 100001 100010 100100 100101
101000 101001 101010

If you want to allow two 1's in a row but not three or more, there's an easy way to do that. You just add another state to the previous automaton as shown in figure 2. The added state 2 is reached with two 1's in a row. The start state is still 0 and all of the states are allowable end states. There are 44 such strings of length 6. They are shown below.

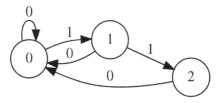

Figure 2: Automaton for strings of 0's and 1's with no repeats of three or more 1's in a row.

000000	000001	000010	000011	000100	000101
000110	001000	001001	001010	001011	001100
001101	010000	010001	010010	010011	010100
010101	010110	011000	011001	011010	011011
100000	100001	100010	100011	100100	100101
100110	101000	101001	101010	101011	101100
101101	110000	110001	110010	110011	110100
110101	110110				

The way to turn strings like this into a melody is to assign notes or chords to each of the possible symbols in a string. In the two examples above there are only two symbols, 0 and 1 to which we could, for example, assign the chords CEG and FAC. There are a number of programs on the book's website that can convert these strings into abc notation from which you can then make a MIDI file. We will describe the general procedure for doing this and then describe each step in more detail.

The first step is to generate the strings using the program `autogen2`.[1] For the first example, where no runs of two or more 1's are allowed, you get $121,393$ strings of length 24. You can't possibly listen to all of them so the second step is to randomly select a subset of them using the program `ssline`.[2] Once you have the strings

---

[1] Details on how to use this program and others are given in the software chapter.

[2] The program `ssline`, whose name refers to *subset lines*, will

you want to listen to, the next step is to use the program `str2abc` to create an abc file. The final step is to convert the abc file into a MIDI file using `abc2midi`.[3]

We will now describe each step for the first example in more detail. To run the `autogen2` program you need to create a file that defines the automaton.[4] For the first example the file is

```
2
0 (0,0) (1,1)
1 (0,0)
```

which we will call `fib.aut2`. The first line in the file is the number of states, which is just 2 as you can see in figure 1. Each subsequent line describes a state and its transitions to other states. The first number on each line identifies the state. States are always numbered starting at 0. Next come pairs of elements enclosed in parentheses that describe transitions. The first element is the number of the state to transition to and

---

sample, with equal probability, a desired number of lines from `stdin`.

[3]The `abc2midi` program is part of a package called `abcMIDI` that can be downloaded from https://ifdo.ca/~seymour/runabc/top.html or https://sourceforge.net/projects/abc/ Documentation is at https://ifdo.ca/~seymour/runabc/abcguide/abc2midi_guide.html

[4]The exact format documentation is described in the software chapter.

the second is the output for the transition. The exact format of these lines is described in detail in the software chapter.

Once you have the automaton file, you can count how many strings of length 24 are produced using the command:

```
autogen2 fib.aut2 24 0 0 1 | wc
```

This command sends the output of `autogen2` to the program `wc`[5] which counts lines, words and characters. In this case `wc` will produce the following output

```
121393 2913432 5948257
```

The first number is the number of lines output by the program `autogen2`. There is one string for each line, so there are $121,393$ strings of length 24 that are produced by the automaton. We can randomly select 10 of them using the command:

```
autogen2 fib.aut2 24 0 0 1 | ssline 121393 10
```

This produces the output

```
000000010101010010101010
000000100100100010010101
000010010001001000100001
```

---

[5]`wc` is available on all Unix systems. On Windows it is part of the GNU CoreUtilities package which you can download from http://gnuwin32.sourceforge.net/packages/coreutils.htm

```
001001010101000001000010
001010101001001010010010
010000000000100000010000
010000000100010101010010
010100000101010101010001
100001000001000001000101
100100010000100001010001
```

We want to listen to only two of these strings so we
select two of them, and create the file **fib1.str** which
consists of the lines:

```
Fibo example 1
Stefan and Richard
Abrazol Publishing
2
[CEG] [FAC]
001001010101000001000010 121221111224 1
001010101001001010010010 121221111224 1
```

The first three lines of the file are just documentation
strings. The next line gives the number of notes or
chords used. This is followed by a line with the notes
or chords in abc notation. The rest of the lines consist
of the strings to be converted into abc notation. Each
line starts with the string followed by the rhythm and
the number of times it is repeated. Full documentation
of the file format can be found in the software chapter.

The file `fib1.str` is turned into an abc file using the command:

```
str2abc fib1.str 24 C 240 1/4 > fib1.abc
```

The file `fib1.abc` is turned into a MIDI file using the command:

```
abc2midi fib1.abc -o fib1.mid
```

You can find these files, and files for all the other examples in this book, on the book's website.

Ternary Automata

Things get more interesting when we move on to strings with three symbols. These can then be translated into melodies with three notes or chords. We will call three symbol strings ternary strings or sequences.

An automaton for ternary strings where each symbol is different from the preceding symbol, i.e. no symbol can repeat itself, is shown in figure 3. The automaton has 4 states. ⓪ is the start state, and ①, ② and ③ are end states.

We will call the automaton description file `tern1.aut2`. It consists of the following lines:

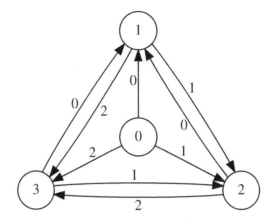

Figure 3: An automaton for strings with 3 symbols and no repeats allowed.

```
0 (1,0) (2,1) (3,2)
1 (2,1) (3,2)
2 (1,0) (3,2)
3 (1,0) (2,1)
```

For this automaton it's easy to calculate the number of strings of length n that it produces. There are 3 possibilities for the first symbol, and 2 possibilities for each subsequent symbol, so the number of strings of length n is $3 \cdot 2^{n-1}$. For $n = 24$ there will be a total of $25,165,824$ strings. We generate them all and randomly sample 10 using the command:

```
autogen2 tern1.aut2 24 0 0 1 2 3 | ssline 25165824 10
```

This produces the following strings

```
01010102120121010212020l
012021010201010121210201
012120120202101012101210
012121021210212121212020
020101020210210210101012
020120102121201021010201
120201021021021212010101
121202101012102102012012
201021010120101201201012
210121012120210121012010
```

Now we create the file **tern1.str** which consists of the following lines:

```
Strings with 3 symbols and no repeats allowed
Stefan and Richard
Abrazol Publishing
3
[CEG] [FAC] [GBD]
01010102120121010212020l 121221111224 1
012021010201010121210201 121221111224 1
012120120202101012101210 121221111224 1
012121021210212121212020 121221111224 1
020101020210210210101012 121221111224 1
020120102121201021010201 121221111224 1
120201021021021212010101 121221111224 1
```

12120210101210210201201 121221111224 1
20102101012010120120101 121221111224 1
21012101212020210121012010 121221111224 1

This is turned into an abc file with the command:

`str2abc tern1.str 24 C 240 1/4 > tern1.abc`

The abc file is turned into a MIDI file with the command:

`abc2midi tern1.abc -o tern1.mid`

You can find these files on the book's website.

A melody where no note or chord ever repeats twice in succession can be interesting but most melodies are not like that, there are repeats. So how do we modify the above automaton to allow each of the symbols to repeat once? You may want to think about this for a minute to see if you can come up with the solution yourself.

The automaton in figure 4 will do the job. It is similar to the previous automaton, but three additional states have been added that correspond to a second 0, 1, or 2. The symbol 0 puts us in ① as in the previous example, but now a second 0 puts us in the new state ④, and similarly for the other symbols.

The files for this example are `tern2.aut2`, `tern2.str` and `tern2.mid`. To make `tern2.str`, we use the same autogen2 command as in the last example to get 10 note strings, then use the same rhythm strings and chords as in tern1.str. Repeating the str2abc command as in the last example, we make tern2.abc, then use abc2midi to make tern2.mid. The files can be found on the book's website.

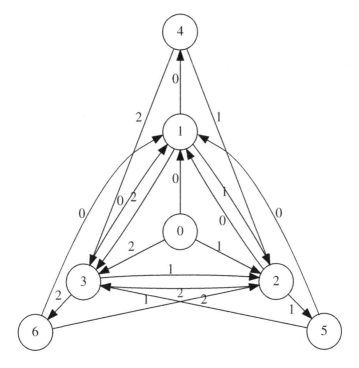

Figure 4: An automaton for strings with 3 symbols and one repeat allowed.

It should be clear how to extend this example to allow

for specific numbers of repeats for each of the symbols. For instance if we want to allow one additional repeat of 0, so that now it is possible to get three 0's in a row, all we have to do is add one more state that ④ in figure 4 can transition to on a 0. That new state then connects to ③ and ② in the same way that ④ does. If you want to allow any number of repeats then you let ①, ② and ③ transition back to themselves as shown in figure 5.

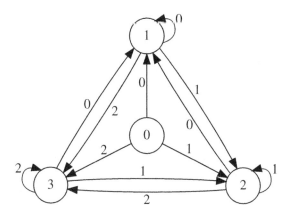

Figure 5: An automaton for strings with 3 symbols, and any number of repeats.

Now we want to look at some examples involving ternary strings with substring restrictions. By following these simple examples you should be able to construct your own automata for generating strings with three or more symbols that have more complex substring restrictions.

Suppose for example that we want to generate ternary strings where a 1 follows a 0 only at the end of the string. The automaton in figure 6 will do the trick. ⓪ is the start state, and ② is the end state. The only way to get to ② is to output a 0 followed by a 1. There are no transitions out of ②, so after the 01, there are no more outputs.

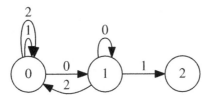

Figure 6: An automaton for ternary strings with 01 only at the end.

If we want to allow a 01 substring to appear prior to the end also, we will need to modify the automaton as shown in figure 7. Once again, ⓪ is the start state and ② is the end state, but now there are transitions out of ② to allow the string to continue after a 01. Still, the string must end in a 01 since ② is the end state, and a 01 always puts us in that state.

The same automaton can be used to generate strings

where a 01 does not appear at the end, by making ⓪ and ① the end states instead of ②.

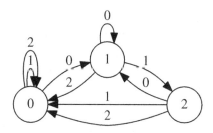

Figure 7: An automaton for ternary strings with 01 at the end.

See if you can construct an automaton that produces ternary strings where the substring 012 occurs only at the end of the string. The automaton shown in figure 8 will do the trick. The start state is ⓪ and the end state is ③. The only way to get to ③ is by outputting the string 012. The automaton outputs 26 strings of length 6. They are:

```
000012  001012  002012  010012  011012  020012
021012  022012  100012  101012  102012  110012
111012  112012  120012  121012  122012  200012
201012  202012  210012  211012  212012  220012
221012  222012
```

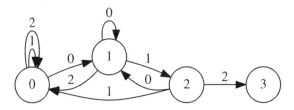

Figure 8: An automaton for ternary strings ending with 012 and no other occurrences of 012.

Can you figure out how to change the automaton to allow 012 to occur before the end also? The answer is shown in figure 9. All that's needed is to add transitions out of ③ to allow the automaton to continue. The end state is still ③ so that the string always ends with 012.

How about strings that don't allow 012 anywhere in the string? For that you can use the automaton in figure

8 but instead of making ③ the end state you make ⓪, ①, and ② the end states.

These ternary examples can be extended to cases where you have four or more symbols. In all cases you can construct automata that place a substring only at the beginning, end or middle of the output string. You can also make it so that the substring does not appear anywhere in the output. Making the substring appear a given number of times is also possible.

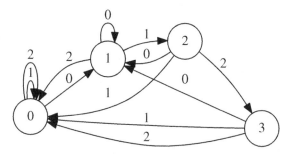

Figure 9: An automaton for ternary strings ending with 012.

These kinds of automata will allow you to experiment with melodies where you have a particular note sequence and you want to try to lead up to or follow it with all possible other note sequences. Note however that when the sequence length gets large there may be too many possibilities to try them all. In that case you can randomly choose a subset using the `ssline` program that we used in the binary string examples above.

Diatonic Scale: single octave

Now we want to look at a few examples of automata with seven states. These can be used to create melodies that use all seven notes in a diatonic scale.

Let's start with the simple automaton shown in figure 10. The states are connected linearly with two end states, ⓪ and ⑥, that always transition to one other state. In between there are 5 states that can transition to 2 other states.

There are a number of ways to use this automaton. We can start and stop at one of the ends. We can start at one end and stop at the other. We can also start somewhere between the ends and stop at one of the ends. We will look at a few examples.

In table 1 we have the number of sequences that can be generated when starting at ⓪ and ending at ⓪, ①, ②, ③, ④, ⑤, ⑥. There are a few things to note. First of all in each column we have either all the even or all the odd length sequences equal to 0. For example

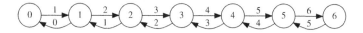

Figure 10: A linear automaton with seven states.

the length of sequences returning to ⓪ must be even. You can't return to ⓪ with an odd number of steps (transitions).

The table also shows that the number of sequences of length n that end at ⓪ is equal to the number of sequences of length $n-1$ that end at ①. This is because to be at ⓪ at step n you must be at ① at step $n-1$. The same kind of thing applies to ending at ⑤ or ⑥. The number of sequences of length n that end at ⑥ is equal to the number of sequences of length $n-1$ that end at ⑤. So you won't get anything significantly different by ending at one or the other.

If you want a sequence in which all seven numbers appear (all notes in the scale are used) then you are unlikely to get one by starting and stopping at ⓪ unless the sequence is very long. For lengths less than 12 there are no such sequences. For length 12 there is only one sequence that includes all numbers, the sequence 123456543210. Table 2 shows the number of sequences that contain all the numbers and their fraction of the total. The percentage of sequences that contain all

n	End Node						
	0	1	2	3	4	5	6
2	1	0	1	0	0	0	0
3	0	2	0	1	0	0	0
4	2	0	3	0	1	0	0
5	0	5	0	4	0	1	0
6	5	0	9	0	5	0	1
7	0	14	0	14	0	6	0
8	14	0	28	0	20	0	6
9	0	42	0	48	0	26	0
10	42	0	90	0	74	0	26
11	0	132	0	164	0	100	0
12	132	0	296	0	264	0	100
13	0	428	0	560	0	364	0
14	428	0	988	0	924	0	364
15	0	1416	0	1912	0	1288	0
16	1416	0	3328	0	3200	0	1288
17	0	4744	0	6528	0	4488	0
18	4744	0	11272	0	11016	0	4488
19	0	16016	0	22288	0	15504	0
20	16016	0	38304	0	37792	0	15504
21	0	54320	0	76096	0	53296	0
22	54320	0	130416	0	129392	0	53296
23	0	184736	0	259808	0	182688	0
24	184736	0	444544	0	442496	0	182688
25	0	629280	0	887040	0	625184	0
26	629280	0	1516320	0	1512224	0	625184
27	0	2145600	0	3028544	0	2137408	0
28	2145600	0	5174144	0	5165952	0	2137408
29	0	7319744	0	10340096	0	7303360	0
30	7319744	0	17659840	0	17643456	0	7303360
31	0	24979584	0	35303296	0	24946816	0
32	24979584	0	60282880	0	60250112	0	24946816
33	0	85262464	0	120532992	0	85196928	0
34	85262464	0	205795456	0	205729920	0	85196928
35	0	291057920	0	411525376	0	290926848	0
36	291057920	0	702583296	0	702452224	0	290926848

Table 1: The number of sequences of length n that begin at ⓪ and end at ⓪,①,②,③,④,⑤,⑥.

n	Total	All numbers	Fraction
2	1	0	0
4	2	0	0
6	5	0	0
8	14	0	0
10	42	0	0
12	132	1	0.00757
14	428	11	0.02570
16	1416	75	0.05297
18	4744	410	0.08642
20	16016	1975	0.12331
22	54320	8778	0.16159
24	184736	36938	0.19995
26	629280	149501	0.23757
28	2145600	587951	0.27403
30	7319744	2262375	0.30908
32	24979584	8558854	0.34263
34	85262464	31945379	0.37467
36	291057920	117939506	0.40521

Table 2: Number of sequences of length n that begin and end at ⓪, number of such sequences that include all numbers, fraction of the total.

the numbers increases with the length of the sequence, reaching about 40% for sequences of length 36.

The following command will generate all strings of length 30 that begin and end at ⓪ and then randomly select 10 of them:

```
autogen2 17.aut2 30 0 0 | ssline 7319744 10
```

Only 4 of the sequences produced contain a 6 indicating that all the states had been traversed. Those sequences are:

```
10123434545654323456543234321
12123456565654345434323232321
12345434565654323212323232121
12345654565454343232321012121
```

Using these sequences, we created 17.str which consists of the lines:

```
Strings with 7 symbols and no repeats allowed
Stefan and Richard
Abrazol Publishing
7
C [^AG^D] [FD^A] [CAF] [GEC] [DBG] [A^FD]
10123434545654323456543234321000 2112 1
12123456565654345434323232321000 2112 1
12345434565654323212323232121000 2112 1
12345654565454343232321012121000 2112 1
```

Note that we've appended a couple 0's to the end of the note strings to make the length 32 which is evenly divisible by the rhythm string length of 4. The following commands were used to generate the MIDI file:

```
str2abc 17.str 24 C 240 1/4 > 17.abc
abc2midi 17.abc -o 17.mid
```

The result is a melody that sounds a bit suspenseful. You can listen to it on the book's website. [6]

Notice that in the first and last of the above sequences there is a return to ⓪ before the end of the sequence, i.e. there is a 0 in the sequence before the end. One variation is to not allow a return to ⓪ until the very end. We will leave it to you to figure out how to generate such sequences.[7] The number of such sequences is shown in table 3.

Other variations are to allow a certain number of repeats for the different states. We showed how to do that in the previous examples with ternary sequences. From those examples it should be clear how the automaton in figure 10 should be modified.

If you want to allow an unlimited number of repeats for each state you can simply add a transition from each state back to itself as shown in figure 11. The number of such sequences that begin at ⓪ and end at ⓪, ①,

---

[6]Notes can be assigned in many different ways. One particularly nice way is:

0	1	2	3	4	5	6
C	E	G	B	A	F	D

Another way is to use the three note chords of the Circle of Major Triads shown in the Notes and Chords section near the end of this book.

[7]Hint: create another linear automaton like that in figure 10 but with one less state.

n	Number of Sequences
2	1
4	1
6	2
8	5
10	14
12	42
14	131
16	417
18	1341
20	4334
22	14041
24	45542
26	147798
28	479779
30	1557649
32	5057369
34	16420730
36	53317085

Table 3: Number of sequences of length n that begin at ⓪ and return to ⓪ for the first time at the end of the sequence.

②, ③, ④, ⑤, ⑥ is shown in table 4.

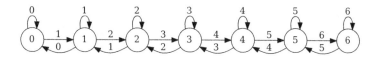

Figure 11: A linear automaton with seven states and any number of repeats allowed.

Instead of a linear connection of states, we could use a circular connection as shown in figure 12. Now all states are equivalent in the sense that they all have transitions to two other states. The number of sequences that start at ⓪ and end at ⓪, ①, ②, and ③ is shown in table 5.

To allow any number of repeats, we just put a feedback loop on each one of the states in figure 12. This gives us the automaton in figure 13. The number of sequences that start at ⓪ and end at ⓪, ①, ②, and ③ is shown in table 6.

n	End Node						
	0	1	2	3	4	5	6
1	1	1	0	0	0	0	0
2	2	2	1	0	0	0	0
3	4	5	3	1	0	0	0
4	9	12	9	4	1	0	0
5	21	30	25	14	5	1	0
6	51	76	69	44	20	6	1
7	127	196	189	133	70	27	7
8	323	512	518	392	230	104	34
9	835	1353	1422	1140	726	368	138
10	2188	3610	3915	3288	2234	1232	506
11	5798	9713	10813	9437	6754	3972	1738
12	15511	26324	29963	27004	20163	12464	5710
13	41835	71798	83291	77130	59631	38337	18174
14	113633	196924	232219	220052	175098	116142	56511
15	310557	542776	649195	627369	511292	347751	172653
16	853333	1502528	1819340	1787856	1486412	1031696	520404
17	2355861	4175201	5109724	5093608	4305964	3038512	1552100
18	6531062	11640786	14378533	14509296	12438084	8896576	4590612
19	18171848	32550381	40528615	41325913	35843956	25925272	13487188
20	50722229	91250844	114404909	117698484	103095141	75256416	39412460
21	141973073	256377982	323354237	335198534	296050041	217764017	114668876
22	398351055	721705292	914930753	954602812	849012592	628482934	332432893

Table 4: The number of sequences of length n that begin at ⓪ and end at ⓪,①,②,③,④,⑤,⑥ with any number of repeats allowed.

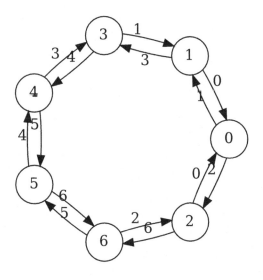

Figure 12: A seven state automaton in a circular geometry.

	End Node			
n	0	1	2	3
1	0	1	0	0
2	2	0	1	0
3	0	3	0	1
4	6	0	4	1
5	0	10	1	5
6	20	1	15	6
7	2	35	7	21
8	70	9	56	28
9	18	126	37	84
10	252	55	210	121
11	110	462	176	331
12	924	286	793	507
13	572	1717	793	1300
14	3434	1365	3017	2093
15	2730	6451	3458	5110
16	12902	6188	11561	8568
17	12376	24463	14756	20129
18	48926	27132	44592	34885
19	54264	93518	62017	79477
20	187036	116281	172995	141494
21	232562	360031	257775	314489
22	720062	490337	674520	572264
23	980674	1394582	1062601	1246784
24	2789164	2043275	2641366	2309385
25	4086550	5430530	4352660	4950751
26	10861060	8439210	10381281	9303411
27	16878420	21242341	17742621	19684692
28	42484682	34621041	40927033	37427313
29	69242082	83411715	72048354	78354346
30	166823430	141290436	161766061	150402700
31	282580872	328589491	291693136	312168761
32	657178982	574274008	640758252	603861897
33	1148548016	1297937234	1178135905	1244620149
34	2595874468	2326683921	2542557383	2422756054
35	4653367842	5138431851	4749439975	4965313437
36	10276863702	9402807817	10103745288	9714753412

Table 5: The number of sequences of length n that begin at ⓪ and end at ⓪,①,② and ③ for the automaton in figure 12.

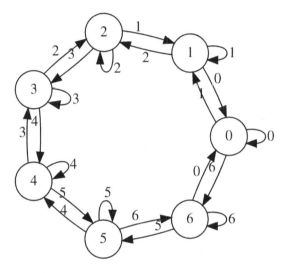

Figure 13: A seven state automaton in a circular geometry with any number of repeats allowed.

	End Node			
n	0	1	2	3
1	1	1	0	0
2	3	2	1	0
3	7	6	3	1
4	19	16	10	5
5	51	45	31	20
6	141	127	96	71
7	395	364	294	238
8	1123	1053	896	770
9	3229	3072	2719	2436
10	9373	9020	8227	7591
11	27413	26620	24838	23409
12	80653	78871	74867	71656
13	238395	234391	225394	218179
14	707177	698180	677964	661752
15	2103537	2083321	2037896	2001468
16	6270179	6224754	6122685	6040832
17	18719687	18617618	18388271	18204349
18	55954923	55725576	55210238	54796969
19	167406075	166890737	165732783	164804176
20	501187549	500029595	497427696	495341135
21	1501246739	1498644840	1492798426	1488109966
22	4498536419	4492690005	4479553232	4469018358
23	13483916429	13470779656	13441261595	13417589948
24	40425475741	40395957680	40329631199	40276441491

Table 6: The number of sequences of length n that begin at ⓪ and end at ⓪,①,② and ③ for the automaton in figure 13.

Diatonic Scale: two octaves

One way to use two octaves of a diatonic scale is to use
two of the linear automata we used for a single octave
and connect them together in a ladder configuration as
shown in figure 14.

We can let each state in the lower line of seven states
represent one of the notes in a diatonic scale and the
state it is connected to in the upper line represent the
same note one octave up in frequency. Of course this is
just one way of interpreting the states as notes. There
are countless other ways to interpret them.

The number of sequences that start at ③ and end at
⓪, ①, ②, and ③ is shown in table 7. The number of
sequences that start at ③ and end at ⑦, ⑧, ⑨, and
⑩ is shown in table 8.

The automaton file for figure 14 is 172.aut2. Using
this with program autogen2, we selected 20 sequences
of length 16 from the 1,787,856 (approximately 1.8
million) possibilities using the following command line:

```
autogen2 172.aut2 16 3 7 | ssline 1787856 20
```

The sequences all start at ③ and end at ⑦. The 20
sequences are:

```
212129a329a92987  234543a323a32187  234bcba981292987
23a3aba9a34ba987  23ab4ba921870107  2929a32923212107
```

```
2987010123a98987  2987878189292187  29a9898107870187
29ab434543298107  43454ba981218107  43a98129a9898787
45cb4ba929210187  4b4ba3a321870107  4bababc543212187
a3434ba321818707  a3a9870181892987  a3abc5cb43a32187
a9aba32187878707  ab4ba3a929898987
```

Note that we use the letters abcd for the transitions to
⓪, ①, ②, and ③.

To create a MIDI file from these strings, we used the
file 172.str shown below:

```
Strings with 14 symbols and no repeats allowed
Stefan and Richard
Abrazol Publishing
14
C G D A E B ^F c g d a e b ^f
212129a329a92987  1212211112211114  1
234543a323a32187  1212211112211114  1
234bcba981292987  1212211112211114  1
23a3aba9a34ba987  1212211112211114  1
23ab4ba921870107  1212211112211114  1
2929a32923212107  1212211112211114  1
2987010123a98987  1212211112211114  1
2987878189292187  1212211112211114  1
29a9898107870187  1212211112211114  1
29ab434543298107  1212211112211114  1
43454ba981218107  1212211112211114  1
43a98129a9898787  1212211112211114  1
45cb4ba929210187  1212211112211114  1
```

```
4b4ba3a321870107 1212211112211114 1
4bababc543212187 1212211112211114 1
a3434ba321818707 1212211112211114 1
a3a9870181892987 1212211112211114 1
a3abc5cb43a32187 1212211112211114 1
a9aba32187878707 1212211112211114 1
ab4ba3a929898987 1212211112211114 1
```

The commands used for making the MIDI file are:

```
str2abc 172.str 24 C 240 1/4 > 172.abc
abc2midi 172.abc -o 172.mid
```

You can listen to the result on the book's website.

An alternative is to connect the two octaves in a circular geometry as shown in figure 15. The number of sequences that start at ⓪ and end at ⓪, ①, ②, and ③ is shown in table 9. The number of sequences that start at ⓪ and end at ⑦, ⑧, ⑨, and ⑩ is shown in table 10.

The automaton file for figure 15 is `c72.aut2`. Using this with program `autogen2`, we selected 20 sequences of length 16 from the 3,479,168 (approximately 3.5 million) possibilities using the following command line:

```
autogen2 c72.aut2 16 0 10 | ssline 3479168 20
```

The sequences all start at ⓪ and end at ⑩. The 20 sequences are:

```
106070187878789a  12123a923a323a9a  123212923234baba
1234b454b4ba343a  123aba3a32923aba  18707012189ababa
1898923ab4b43aba  60123a929a9a989a  60187012323a989a
60189a343234543a  607d6012329a323a  6565607d7dcd789a
656d781012343a9a  6d7d701818923aba  701212989212343a
70601810129abcba  70789ab43ab43a9a  787012981212323a
7d60607d6d60789a  7d6d70123a98189a
```

Note that we use the letters abcd for the transitions to
⓪, ①, ②, and ③.

To create a MIDI file from these strings, we used the
file c72.str shown below:

```
Strings with 14 symbols and no repeats allowed
Stefan and Richard
Abrazol Publishing
14
C G D A E B ^F c g d a e b ^f
106070187878789a 1212211112211114 1
12123a923a323a9a 1212211112211114 1
123212923234baba 1212211112211114 1
1234b454b4ba343a 1212211112211114 1
123aba3a32923aba 1212211112211114 1
18707012189ababa 1212211112211114 1
1898923ab4b43aba 1212211112211114 1
60123a929a9a989a 1212211112211114 1
60187012323a989a 1212211112211114 1
60189a343234543a 1212211112211114 1
607d6012329a323a 1212211112211114 1
```

```
6565607d7dcd789a 1212211112211114 1
656d781012343a9a 1212211112211114 1
6d7d701818923aba 1212211112211114 1
701212989212343a 1212211112211114 1
70601810129abcba 1212211112211114 1
70789ab43ab43a9a 1212211112211114 1
787012981212323a 1212211112211114 1
7d60607d6d60789a 1212211112211114 1
7d6d70123a98189a 1212211112211114 1
```

The commands used for making the MIDI file are:

```
str2abc c72.str 24 C 240 1/4 > c72.abc
abc2midi c72.abc -o c72.mid
```

You can listen to the result on the book's website.

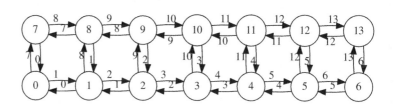

Figure 14: An automaton for two octaves of the diatonic scale.

42

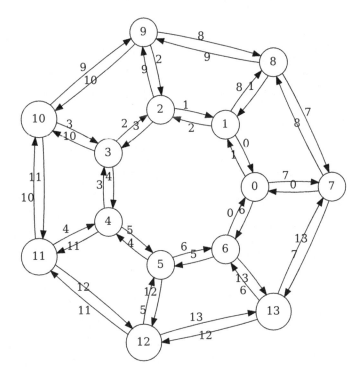

Figure 15: An automaton for two octaves of the diatonic scale connected in a circular geometry.

	End Node			
n	0	1	2	3
1	0	0	1	0
2	0	1	0	3
3	1	0	6	0
4	0	10	0	19
5	14	0	45	0
6	0	89	0	141
7	133	0	356	0
8	0	748	0	1105
9	1140	0	2861	0
10	0	6149	0	8843
11	9437	0	23122	0
12	0	50126	0	71347
13	77130	0	187265	0
14	0	407317	0	577461
15	627369	0	1517896	0
16	0	3305752	0	4679489
17	5093608	0	12307321	0
18	0	26816617	0	37938291
19	41325913	0	99801566	0
20	0	217500050	0	307634739
21	335198534	0	809340533	0
22	0	1763943345	0	2494727293
23	2718546157	0	6563461676	0
24	0	14305345028	0	20231232721

Table 7: The number of sequences of length n that begin at ③ and end at ⓪,①,② and ③ for the automaton in figure 14.

	End Node			
n	7	8	9	10
2	0	0	2	0
3	0	3	0	7
4	4	0	16	0
5	0	30	0	51
6	44	0	126	0
7	0	259	0	393
8	392	0	1008	0
9	0	2148	0	3121
10	3288	0	8130	0
11	0	17567	0	25103
12	27004	0	65792	0
13	0	142922	0	202931
14	220052	0	533118	0
15	0	1160487	0	1643697
16	1787856	0	4322080	0
17	0	9415688	0	13323649
18	14509296	0	35046658	0
19	0	76372571	0	108031607
20	117698484	0	284205744	0
21	0	619404278	0	876046227
22	954602812	0	2304791038	0
23	0	5023337195	0	7104309369
24	7741883352	0	18691108240	0

Table 8: The number of sequences of length n that begin at ③ and end at ⑦,⑧,⑨ and ⑩ for the automaton in figure 14.

n	End Node 0	1	2	3
2	3	0	1	0
3	0	6	0	1
4	19	0	10	1
5	0	45	1	15
6	141	1	90	21
7	2	357	28	161
8	1107	37	784	266
9	90	2907	415	1554
10	8953	670	6765	2851
11	1760	24068	4983	14356
12	73789	9295	58279	28392
13	25454	201644	54275	129935
14	616229	112476	502698	272454
15	315900	1704631	560196	1164450
16	5196899	1254786	4346781	2561664
17	3582852	14513648	5592354	10387613
18	44164131	13279176	37697178	23796703
19	38349144	124307709	54588939	92494147
20	377672349	135521111	327945700	219393115
21	394557422	1070126533	524396222	823286835
22	3246942383	1347471951	2861815572	2012506188
23	3946537938	9253976009	4977715799	7330833930
24	28045330509	13141057384	25048355735	18395305747

Table 9: The number of sequences of length n that begin at ⓪ and end at ⓪,①,② and ③ for the automaton in figure 15.

	End Node			
n	7	8	9	10
2	0	2	0	0
3	7	0	3	0
4	0	16	0	4
5	51	0	30	5
6	0	126	6	50
7	393	7	266	77
8	16	1016	112	504
9	3139	165	2304	882
10	420	8350	1462	4740
11	25653	2552	19855	9053
12	6864	69576	16588	43264
13	212941	32747	171119	88244
14	90948	585704	175266	389298
15	1787637	378690	1477700	837018
16	1073280	4969968	1775904	3479168
17	15136835	4103970	12795917	7816736
18	11790792	42446400	17513060	31000266
19	129056931	42583028	111143844	72310029
20	123515200	364508484	169481996	275948020
21	1106689317	428518307	968402204	664823131
22	1251594036	3145218054	1617737660	2456512170
23	9537378491	4216803647	8463545796	6086756018
24	12380145232	27254900296	15281275464	21881135744

Table 10: The number of sequences of length n that begin at ⓪ and end at ⑦,⑧,⑨ and ⑩ for the automaton in figure 15.

Adding a Rhythm

Before continuing with applications of automata we are going to look at a quick example of how to generate a rhythm. For many more examples see our book *Creating Rhythms*.

There are many different ways that a rhythm can be added to a sequence of notes. As an example let's assume we have a sequence of 7 notes to which we want to assign a total of 12 beats, where one beat represents an eighth note. Let n_i be the number of beats assigned to the ith note in the sequence, then the sum of all the n_i must equal 12. If we limit ourselves to eighth notes $n_i = 1$, quarter notes $n_i = 2$, dotted quarter notes $n_i = 3$, and half notes $n_i = 4$, then one set of possible rhythms is:

$$
\begin{array}{ccccccc}
1 & 1 & 1 & 1 & 1 & 3 & 4 \\
1 & 1 & 1 & 1 & 2 & 2 & 4 \\
1 & 1 & 1 & 1 & 2 & 3 & 3 \\
1 & 1 & 1 & 2 & 2 & 2 & 3 \\
1 & 1 & 2 & 2 & 2 & 2 & 2 \\
\end{array}
$$

Mathematically, these rhythms come from partitioning the number 12 into 7 parts where the parts are limited to the sizes 1, 2, 3, 4. The program **partam**, available on the *Creating Rhythms* website, will calculate all partitions of a number n into m parts of allowed sizes. The above rhythms were generated with the command:

```
partam 12 7 1 2 3 4
```

For a partition the order of the parts is irrelevant so if we switch the order of 3 and 4 in the first rhythm it's still the same partition but a very different rhythm. To get all possible orderings of the parts you must calculate what are called compositions. The program compam, available on the *Creating Rhythms* website, will calculate all compositions of a number n into m parts of allowed sizes. For this example the command:

```
compam 12 7 1 2 3 4
```

will produce 413 possible rhythms, but some of them differ only by cyclic shifts. Rhythms that differ by cyclic shifts will sound the same when repeated. They are essentially duplicate rhythms and you may want to remove them. The following command will produce only rhythms that are cyclically unique:

```
neckam 12 7 1 2 3 4
```

The program neckam is available on the *Creating Rhythms* website. The program name comes from the word *necklace*. A necklace is the same no matter what its orientation. The program produces only unique necklaces. Running the above command shows that the possible rhythms is reduced from 413 to 59. The rhythms are:

```
1111134  1111143  1111224  1111233  1111242  1111314
1111323  1111332  1111413  1111422  1112124  1112133
1112142  1112214  1112223  1112232  1112313  1112322
1112412  1113114  1113123  1113132  1113213  1113222
1113312  1114113  1114122  1114212  1121124  1121133
1121142  1121214  1121223  1121232  1121313  1121322
1121412  1122114  1122123  1122132  1122213  1122222
1122312  1123113  1123122  1123212  1131132  1131213
1131222  1131312  1132122  1132212  1141212  1212123
1212132  1212213  1212222  1213122  1221222
```

If you're interested in a more general discussion of rhythms, see our book *Creating Rhythms*. The book presents many unique ways to generate rhythms.

Variations on a Theme

We are now going to look at how to use an automaton to create variations on a piece of music. The piece we are going to look at is inspired by the 2nd movement of Beethoven's Pathetique sonata. In particular, we are going to construct an automaton based on a simplification of the first four measures of the 2nd movement. Those first four measures are:

Pathetique Opening

Beethoven

The note sequence of these first four measures in scientific pitch notation is:

$$A_5 \; D_5 \; E_5 \; F_5 \; G_5 \; C_5^{\#} \; F_5 \; E_5 \; D_5 \; C_5 \; B_4 \; D_5 \; C_5$$

There are a total of 13 notes, 8 of which are unique. In order to construct an automaton, we have to assign numbers to the unique notes. We assign the numbers as follows:

$$B_4 \rightarrow 0$$
$$C_5 \rightarrow 1$$
$$C_5^{\#} \rightarrow 2$$
$$D_5 \rightarrow 3$$
$$E_5 \rightarrow 4$$
$$F_5 \rightarrow 5$$
$$G_5 \rightarrow 6$$
$$A_5 \rightarrow 7$$

Now we can translate the sequence of notes in the sonata into a number sequence as follows: 7345625431031. The corresponding rhythm, with a 1/16 note equal to one beat, is given by the sequence: 8611888222288.

The note numbers are the states in the automaton shown in figure 16. The transitions between states are given by the transitions in the sonata, except for the ③ to ⑦ transition which we added to allow the melody to return to its starting note. The automaton file is `pathetique.aut2` on the book's website.

You can get the automaton to generate the sonata sequence plus many variations by starting at ⑦ and ending at ① and allowing it to run for 12 transitions. Each generated sequence then has a 7 added to the beginning. There are a total of 119 sequences generated using the command:

```
autogen2 pathetique.aut2 12 7 1
```

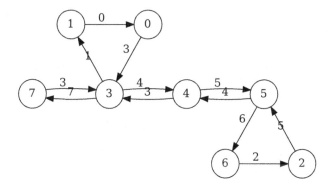

Figure 16: An automaton based on the opening of the 2nd movement of Beethoven's Pathetique.

One way to narrow down the number of sequences is to keep only those with a given subsequence. In the sonata sequence we have the subsequence 3456. If we keep only those sequences in which 3456 appears, then we are left with only 3. After adding a 7 to the beginning of each, those 3 sequences are:

7345625431031
7310345625431
7345625625431

where the original sequence is the first one. We put these in the file **pathetique1.str** as shown below:

Pathetique and variations
Beethoven
Abrazol Publishing
8
B c ^c d e f g a
7345625431031 8611888222288 2
7310345625431 8611888222288 2
7345625625431 8611888222288 2

then we created the MIDI file pathetique1.mid with the commands:

```
str2abc pathetique1.str 24 C 120 1/16 > pathetique1.abc
abc2midi pathetique1.abc -o pathetique1.mid
```

You can listen to the MIDI file on the book's website.

Many other variations are possible. For example there's no need to stop at ①. You can stop at any of the other states. Table 11 gives the number of sequences of lengths 4 through 24 that start at ⑦ and end at any of the states.

As an example, from table 11, we see that there are 32 sequences of length 12 that begin at ⑦ and end at ②. Those 32 sequences are generated by the command:

```
autogen2 pathetique.aut2 12 7 2
```

After adding a 7 to the beginning of each, those 32 sequences are:

n	End Node							
	0	1	2	3	4	5	6	7
4	0	2	0	1	3	0	1	2
5	2	1	1	5	1	3	0	1
6	1	5	0	4	8	2	3	5
7	5	4	3	14	6	8	2	4
8	4	14	2	15	22	9	8	14
9	14	15	8	40	24	24	9	15
10	15	40	9	53	64	32	24	40
11	40	53	24	119	85	73	32	53
12	53	119	32	178	192	109	73	119
13	119	178	73	364	287	224	109	178
14	178	364	109	584	588	360	224	364
15	364	584	224	1130	944	697	360	584
16	584	1130	360	1892	1827	1168	697	1130
17	1130	1892	697	3541	3060	2187	1168	1892
18	1892	3541	1168	6082	5728	3757	2187	3541
19	3541	6082	2187	11161	9839	6896	3757	6082
20	6082	11161	3757	19462	18057	12026	6896	11161
21	11161	19462	6896	35300	31488	21814	12026	19462
22	19462	35300	12026	62111	57114	38384	21814	35300
23	35300	62111	21814	111876	100495	69140	38384	62111
24	62111	111876	38384	197906	181016	122309	69140	111876

Table 11: The number of sequences of length n that begin at ⑦ and end at ⓪ through ⑦ for the automaton in figure 16.

7310343434562 7310343454562 7310343734562 7310345434562
7310345454562 7310373434562 7310373454562 7310373734562
7343103434562 7343103454562 7343103734562 7343431034562
7343434562562 7343454562562 7343456254562 7343731034562
7343734562562 7345431034562 7345434562562 7345454562562
7345456254562 7345625434562 7345625454562 7373103434562
7373103454562 7373103734562 7373431034562 7373434562562
7373454562562 7373456254562 7373731034562 7373734562562

As before, we put these in the file pathetique2.str
and ran the following commands to create the MIDI
file pathetique2.mid which you can listen to on the
book's website.

```
str2abc pathetique2.str 24 C 120 1/16 > pathetique2.abc
abc2midi pathetique2.abc -o pathetique2.mid
```

You can use this same process on other pieces of music
to generate melodies in the same style as the original.

PROBABILISTIC AUTOMATA

We saw in the last chapter that the number of melodies produced by an automaton often becomes extremely large as the length increases. There's no way to listen to all of them, but we can randomly sample from the complete set. There are two ways to do it.

The first way was covered in the last chapter where we used the program `ssline` to select a random subset of all the output strings produced by the automaton. The assumption behind this selection process is that every string has the same probability. Suppose however that we want some strings to have a higher probability than others. How do we do that?

The most general way to do it is to assign probabilities to each transition of each state. Then instead of exhaustively following all the paths from a start state to an end state, you randomly follow a path based on the probabilities. This is equivalent to the first way only when each state has the same number of transitions and they all have the same probability.

The advantage of this method is that you can make some transitions more or less probable than others, which is the way things are in music. You are more likely to find some note or chord progressions in certain styles of music than in others. Some composers tend to favor some progressions more than others as we will see in an example below.

There's a good analogy between this and the structure of the English language. If you look at the spelling of words, for example, the letter u almost always follows the letter q. If you misspell things too badly no one will be able to make sense of what you are trying to say. This is true in both language and music. Music is after all a kind of language.

We will call an automaton that has probabilities assigned to its state transitions a probabilistic automaton. An example of a simple three state probabilistic automaton whose states are the notes of the C-major chord (CEG) is shown in figure 17. The transitions in the figure are labeled with their probabilities.

For this particular automaton you can see that there's a probability of 0.5 that it remains in any state that it's in, and equal probabilities of 0.25 that it transitions to one of the other two states. For example when the automaton is in state C the probability that it outputs a C and remains in state C is 0.5. The probability that it outputs an E and transitions to state E is 0.25. The probability that it outputs a G and transitions to state G is 0.25.

An important thing to keep in mind about these automata is that the sum of the probabilities for all the transitions out of a state must equal 1.

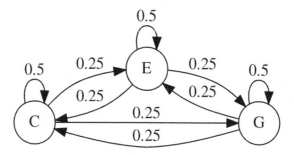

Figure 17: A simple three state probabilistic automaton.

Generating the strings of a probabilistic automaton can be done using the program **pautogen** whose name stands for *probabilistic automaton generator*. The program needs a simple text file that describes the automaton. The file (`ceg1.pat`) for the three state example in figure 17 is:

```
3
0 (0,0,0.5) (1,1,0.25) (2,2,0.25)
1 (1,1,0.5) (0,0,0.25) (2,2,0.25)
2 (2,2,0.5) (1,1,0.25) (0,0,0.25)
```

where the states CEG are represented by integers 0,1,2 respectively. This file is very similar to the files used to describe a regular automaton.

The first line of the file contains a single number indicating the number of states in the automaton. Each successive line describes a state and its transitions. The lines begin with a state number. The first state must always be 0 and the states must be numbered consecutively. The state number is followed by a description of the state's transitions. A transition is described by three elements separated by commas inside a pair of parentheses. The first element is the number of the state that is transitioned to. The second element is the transition output string. The last element is the transition probability.

Using this file a sequence of 100 states/notes can be generated with the command:

```
pautogen ceg1.pat 100 0 137
```

where the numbers following the filename are respectively, the length of the output sequence (100), the start state (0), and the random number seed (137). The random number seed is used to allow for repeatability. A given random number seed will generate the same string every time. The seed can be any integer from 1 to 4294967295. The output of the above command is:

```
0112220001100122212122220110120111022220011111
2202202220221111101011120000101121111110002120
02121121
```

This output represents notes CEG where the correspondence is 0 →C, 1 →E, and 2 →G.

To play these notes, we need a rhythm string. We can create one with another simple probabilistic automaton described by the file rhythm01.pat as follows:[8]

```
1
0 (0,4,0.1875) (0,22,0.25) (0,211,0.125)
  (0,121,0.125) (0,112,0.125) (0,1111,0.1875)
```

---

[8] The last two lines are on one line in the actual file.

We are using common 4/4 time here so that the number 4 represents a whole note, 2 represents a half note, and 1 represents a quarter note. The automaton has only one state (0) from which there are six possible outputs $(4, 22, 211, 121, 112, 1111)$ with corresponding probabilities. There's only one state because the probability of each output is independent of previous outputs, i.e. there are no conditional probabilities.

We can generate a length 20 output sequence, again using program **pautogen** with command:

```
pautogen rhythm01.pat 20 0 13
```

The output is:

121221111412122411211112114444111111111121111224

This rhythm happens to be 48 characters long, so to make a melody using this rhythm and the notes we generated above, we use the first 48 notes, putting them into the **str2abc** program's input file **ceg1.str** which consists of the following lines:[9]

```
CEG example 1
Stefan and Richard
Abrazol Publishing
3
C E G
011222000110012221212222011012011102222001111122
121221111412122411211112114444111111111121111224 1
```

---

[9]The last two lines are on one line in the actual file.

This file has the work's title on the first line, composer on the second line, and the transcriber on the third line. The fourth line has a single number specifying the number of notes/chords that will be used. The fifth line is a space separated list of notes/chords that will be assigned to numbers $0, 1, 2, \ldots$ respectively. Any remaining lines (in this case we have only one) contain first the note string, then the rhythm string, and finally the number of times to repeat the line. Using this file, we can now generate an abc file, then MIDI file with commands:

```
str2abc ceg1.str 0 C 180 1/4 > ceg1.abc
abc2midi ceg1.abc -o ceg1.mid
```

You can find these files and listen on the book's website.

We can make a more repetitive song-like melody by repeating some of the note string and rhythm string segments as shown in ceg1a.str below

```
CEG example 2
Stefan and Richard
Abrazol Publishing
3
C E G
0112220001 1212211114 2
100122 121224 2
2001111122 1121111224 2
```

We make the MIDI file with the commands:

```
str2abc ceg1a.str 0 C 180 1/4 > ceg1a.abc
abc2midi ceg1a.abc -o ceg1a.mid
```

Note that because we are using 4/4 time and a unit note length of 1/4, the rhythm string must sum to an integer multiple of 4 to have a whole number of measures on each line.

A nice variation on the above example is to replace the C major chord notes "C E G" in `ceg1a.str` with the chords of C major, F major, and G major so we make a new file `ceg1b.str` that is:

```
CEG example 3
Stefan and Richard
Abrazol Publishing
3
[CEG] [FAC] [GBD]
0112220001 1212211114 2
100122 121224 2
2001111122 1121111224 2
```

and we make the MIDI file with the commands:

```
str2abc ceg1b.str 24 C 240 1/4 > ceg1b.abc
abc2midi ceg1b.abc -o ceg1b.mid
```

Note that we have changed the instrument from acoustic grand piano (MIDI program number 0 in timidity) to nylon string acoustic guitar (MIDI program number 24 in timidity) and changed the time from 180 to 240 beats per minute.

You can experiment with more probabilistic automata by taking some of the examples in the previous chapter and adding probabilities to the transitions. But how do you know what probabilities to use? One way is to just experiment. Another way is to use your judgment. A third way is to analyze a collection of music from a particular composer or style of music and extract transition probabilities from it. We go through an example of how to do this in the next section.

A Stephen Foster Automaton

In the book *Music, Physics and Engineering* by Harry F. Olson there is an analysis of the music of Stephen Foster. He did a statistical analysis of 11 songs written by Foster. The probabilities of one, two and three note sequences were estimated. From this data we can create probabilistic automata that produce melodies which sound increasingly similar to Stephen Foster.

The statistics were compiled on the following 12 notes: B_3, $C_4^\#$, D_4, E_4, $F_4^\#$, G_4, $G_4^\#$, A_4, B_4, $C_5^\#$, D_5, $E_5^\#$ where for example $C_4^\#$ indicates middle C sharp.

For the zeroth order approximation we simply use these

notes without looking at their frequency or actual probability of appearing in a Stephen Foster song. In other words we assume all 12 notes have an equal probability of $1/12 = 0.083333$. The automaton only has a single state and the description file sf0.pat is:[10]

```
1
0 (0,0,0.08333) (0,1,0.08333) (0,2,0.08333) (0,3,0.08333)
  (0,4,0.08333) (0,5,0.08333) (0,6,0.08333) (0,7,0.08333)
  (0,8,0.08333) (0,9,0.08333) (0,a,0.08333) (0,b,0.08333)
```

An example melody is constructed using the output of the command:

```
pautogen sf0.pat 48 0 137
```

whose result was:

```
065a52b43637569547b7a123a7187a98536a5539065513a5
```

Using that note string along with the rhythm string from previous examples:

```
12122111412122411211112114444111111111121111224
```

we created the file sf0.str consisting of the lines:[11]

---

[10]The last three lines are on one line in the actual file.

[11]The last two lines are on one line in the actual file.

```
Stephen Foster Example 0
Stefan and Richard
Abrazol Publishing
12
B, ^C D E ^F G ^G A B ^c d ^e
065a52b43637569547b7a123a7187a98536a5539065513a5
1212211114121224112111121144441111111111121111224 2
```

We then made the MIDI file sf0.mid with the commands:

```
str2abc sf0.str 24 C 240 1/4 > sf0.abc
abc2midi sf0.abc -o sf0.mid
```

You can hear the result on the book's website.

The zeroth order approximation is not a very good representation of Stephen Foster's music. To get better we need to use the actual note probabilities. For the first order approximation we use the note probabilities as shown in the following table.

Note	Probability
B_3	0.0445
$C_4^{\#}$	0.0471
D_4	0.1518
E_4	0.0681
$F_4^{\#}$	0.0995
G_4	0.0602
$G_4^{\#}$	0.0445
A_4	0.1754
B_4	0.1100
$C_5^{\#}$	0.0759
D_5	0.0785
$E_5^{\#}$	0.0445

This is once again a single state automaton and the description file sf1.pat is:[12]

```
1
0 (0,0,0.0445) (0,1,0.0471) (0,2,0.1518) (0,3,0.0681)
  (0,4,0.0995) (0,5,0.0602) (0,6,0.0445) (0,7,0.1754)
  (0,8,0.1100) (0,9,0.0759) (0,a,0.0785) (0,b,0.0445)
```

To compare this to the zeroth order melody we use the same random number seed of 137 and the same rhythm string. The result can be heard as sf1.mid on the book's website. The melody should be starting to sound just a little like Stephen Foster, at least in regard

---

[12]The last three lines are on one line in the actual file.

to the number of times particular notes are used. But a melody is characterized more by how the notes follow each other than it is by the simple frequency of the notes. To take that into account we need to go to a second order approximation.

For the second order approximation we use the note transition probabilities shown in the following table. The way to interpret the table is as follows. The first row shows that the note B_3 is always followed by the note D_4 because the probability is 1.0 for that transition. Likewise the second row shows that note $C_4^{\#}$ is always followed by D_4. The third row shows that there are 9 possible transitions from D_4. D_4 is followed by B_3 or $C_4^{\#}$ with the probability of 0.0625 and so on. The most probable note following D_4 is E_4. It has a probability of 0.3125.

Second order approximation note transition probabilities

	B_3	$C_4^\#$	D_4	E_4	$F_4^\#$	G_4	$G_4^\#$	A_4	B_4	$C_5^\#$	D_5	$E_5^\#$
B_3	0	0	1.0	0	0	0	0	0	0	0	0	0
$C_4^\#$	0	0	1.0	0	0	0	0	0	0	0	0	0
D_4	0.0625	0.0625	0.125	0.3125	0.1875	0.0625	0	0.0625	0	0.0625	0.0625	0
E_4	0	0.0625	0.375	0.1875	0.25	0	0	0.0625	0	0	0.0625	0
$F_4^\#$	0	0	0.125	0.25	0.3125	0.125	0	0.125	0.0625	0	0	0
G_4	0	0	0	0	0.25	0.1875	0	0.375	0.1875	0	0	0
$G_4^\#$	0	0	0	0	0	0	0	1.0	0	0	0	0
A_4	0	0	0.0625	0	0.3125	0.0625	0.0625	0.25	0.1875	0	0.0625	0
B_4	0	0	0.0625	0	0.0625	0.0625	0	0.5625	0.125	0	0.125	0
$C_5^\#$	0	0	0	0	0	0	0	0.25	0.4375	0.1875	0.0625	0.0625
D_5	0	0	0	0	0	0	0	0	0.5	0	0.5	0
$E_5^\#$	0	0	0	0	0	0	0	0.375	0	0.625	0	0

To implement this with pautogen we need a 12 state automaton, one state for each of the notes. The automaton is defined in the file sf2.pat shown below. A diagram of the automaton is shown in the following figure.

You can compare this with the first order example by once again using the same random number seed of 137 and the same rhythm string. The result is sf2.mid on the book's website.

This should be starting to sound a little more like Stephen Foster than sf1.mid did. But to get closer to his true style, we need to look at probabilities for longer sequences of notes. In his book *Music, Physics and Engineering*, Olson compiled statistics for three note sequences. From this we can get the probability that a particular note follows a sequence of two notes. To represent all such possible transitions requires a 50 state automaton. You can find the automaton file for this on the book's website as sf3.pat. It is too long and complex to list here. The MIDI file sf3.mid was created in the same way as the other approximations. You can listen to it on the book's website.

You could continue this process and look at the statistics of sequences of four or more notes. These statistics should get you even closer to the true style of Stephen Foster. The limitation is that you need more examples of his music for the statistics to be meaningful. For

Probabilistic automaton file sf2.pat

```
12
0  (2,2,1.0)
1  (2,2,1.0)
2  (0,0,0.0625) (1,1,0.0625) (2,2,0.125) (3,3,0.3125) (4,4,0.1875) (5,5,0.0625) (7,7,0.0625)
   (9,9,0.0625) (10,a,0.0625)
3  (1,1,0.0625) (2,2,0.375) (3,3,0.1875) (4,4,0.25) (7,7,0.0625) (10,a,0.0625)
4  (2,2,0.125) (3,3,0.25) (4,4,0.3125) (5,5,0.125) (7,7,0.125) (8,8,0.0625)
5  (4,4,0.25) (5,5,0.1875) (7,7,0.375) (8,8,0.1875)
6  (7,7,1.0)
7  (2,2,0.0625) (4,4,0.3125) (5,5,0.0625) (6,6,0.0625) (7,7,0.25) (8,8,0.1875) (10,a,0.0625)
8  (2,2,0.0625) (4,4,0.0625) (5,5,0.0625) (7,7,0.5625) (8,8,0.125) (10,a,0.125)
9  (8,8,0.5) (10,a,0.5)
10 (7,7,0.25) (8,8,0.4375) (9,9,0.1875) (10,a,0.0625) (11,b,0.0625)
11 (7,7,0.375) (9,9,0.625)
```

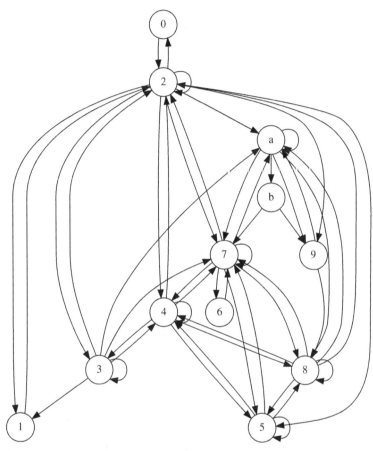

Automaton diagram representing probabilistic automaton file sf2.pat

a musical genre such as Jazz or Blues where you have a data set of thousands of compositions you can easily extend the statistical analysis to longer sequences. Combine this with statistical models of rhythms and you can create many new compositions in that genre.

LATTICES

Lattices offer a visual way to create musical patterns. By a lattice we mean a regular geometric arrangement of nodes (points) in one or more dimensions with the nodes connected to each other in a symmetric and repeated way.

Each node in the lattice represents a note or chord and the connections give the allowable transitions from one note or chord to the next. The connections are usually taken to be bidirectional so if node A is connected to node B it means we can transition from A to B or B to A.

A sequence of notes is generated by starting at some node S and moving along the connections to a final node E. The start and end nodes do not need to be different.

A sequence is called a walk on the lattice between nodes S and E. The number of possible walks of a given length between two nodes is a function of the length and generally increases very rapidly with length.

Looking at a few lattice types will clarify these concepts. The simplest case is one dimension where the only possible lattice is the simple linear lattice shown in figure 18. We looked at some small finite examples of this lattice in the automaton chapter.

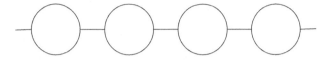

Figure 18: Linear lattice.

The two dimensional version of the linear lattice is the square lattice shown in figure 19. The fret board on a guitar can be interpreted as a square lattice.

Another two dimensional lattice is the triangular lattice shown in figure 20. The bass buttons on an accordion can be interpreted as a triangular lattice.

The three dimensional version of the square lattice is the cubic lattice. There are many other lattices in three or more dimensions but they become increasingly harder to define and work with so we will confine ourselves to two dimensions in this book.

A very simple example of a finite square lattice is shown in figure 21. It consists of 3 rows and columns labeled from 0 to 2. The top row is assigned the notes A, E, B, from left to right. The next row is assigned the notes F, C, G. The bottom row is assigned the chords $[CAF]$, $[GEC]$, $[DBG]$.

To make it easier to generate sequences, the nodes in the lattices will be referred to by pairs of numbers instead of the notes they represent. The node at column i and row j will be represented by the pair of numbers

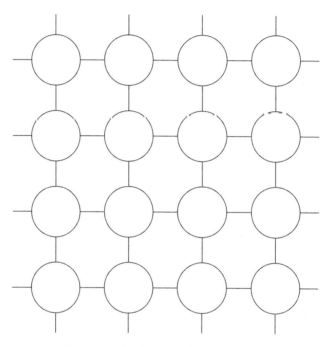

Figure 19: Square lattice.

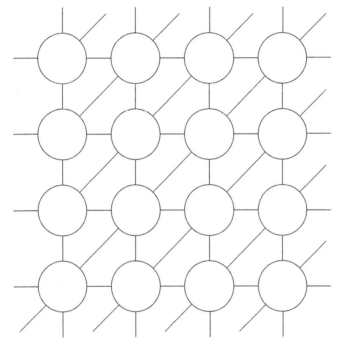

Figure 20: Triangular lattice.

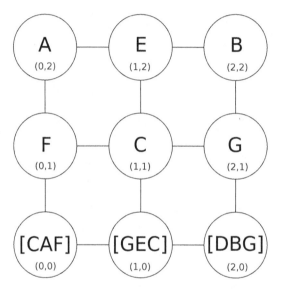

Figure 21: A 3x3 square lattice.

80

(i, j).

We want to look at sequences that start at one node and end at another node. All such sequences of length n can be generated using the program fsquare. The program will generate sequences for any finite size square lattice.

For example, to get all sequences of length 8, starting at $(0, 0)$ and ending at $(2, 2)$, you run the program as follows:

```
fsquare 3 3 0 0 2 2 8
```

The first two parameters are the number of columns and the number of rows. The next two parameters are the column and row of the starting node. The following two parameters are the column and row of the ending node. The last parameter is the length of the walk.[13]

For this example, there are 504 walks of length 8. Each walk is output on a separate line. The first few lines of the output are as follows:

```
rrlrlruu
rrlrluru
rrlrluur
rrlrulru
```

---

[13]There is a similar program called ftri for walks on a finite triangular lattice. The program takes the same parameters as fsquare.

```
rrlrulur
rrlruulr
rrlruudu
rrlruduu
rrllrruu
rrllruru
```

For a square lattice, the walks are given in terms of directions right, left, up, and down, denoted by the letters r, l, u, and d. For example, the path rrlruduu will start at $(0,0)$ then move to $(1,0)$ with a step to the right, $(2,0)$ with another step to the right, $(1,0)$ with a step to the left, and so on. The complete walk in terms of nodes is

$$(0,0) - (1,0) - (2,0) - (1,0) - (2,0) - (2,1) - (2,0) - (2,1) - (2,2)$$

In terms of notes and chords, the walk is

$$[CAF] - [GEC] - [DBG] - [GEC] - [DBG] - G - [DBG] - G - B$$

Oftentimes, as in this case, fsquare produces way more lines than we care to use. In such circumstances, it's nice to sample a certain number of the given walks using the program ssline as we've used in previous chapters. For example, to sample 50 walks from the 504 line output of the fsquare command above, we run the following command:

```
fsquare 3 3 0 0 2 2 8 | ssline 504 50
```

whose output is:

rrlrluru	rurududu	urulrdru
rrlurlur	rulrrlur	uruldrru
rrlurduu	rulrlrur	urududru
rrlulrur	rulrudur	urdlurru
rrullrru	rulurrlr	urdluurr
rrullrur	ruurdlru	urduulrr
rrullurr	ruulrdur	uurrlrlr
rruulrdu	ruuldurr	uurdrlru
rruuldru	ruududur	uurdudru
rrudlruu	rudlurur	uurdduru
rlrlurru	ruduurdu	uudrduru
rlrlurur	ruduudur	uududrur
rlrurulr	urrulrlr	udurrudu
rlruudur	urrdlruu	udurdruu
rlurrlru	urrdluru	uduurlrr
rurllrur	urlrlrur	ududurru
rurlduru	urludrur	

Note that for the sake of conserving space in this book, we put the above output in three columns, whereas the program outputs each walk on its own line. Also, as you likely realize, running program ssline twice on the same input will generally result in different outputs.

We can turn these walks into music using our lat2abc program. This program converts walks on a square or

triangular lattice to melodies in abc notation. It's used
as follows

```
lat2abc inst key tempo file.lat
```

where **inst** is a MIDI instrument number, formally
known as a program number, usually $[1, 2, \ldots 128]$, but
$[0, 1, \ldots 127]$ in timidity. The next parameter, **key**,
is the musical key, e.g. C. The following parameter, **tempo**, is the musical tempo in units of beats per
minute, e.g. 180. The final parameter is a file name
defining the lattice walks, and how the walks are translated to abc notation.

For the walks generated above, we created a file called
3x3.lat, of which the first few lines are shown below

```
3 3
[CAF] [GEC] [DBG]
F C G
A E B
0 0 rrlrluru 111221355 1 z1
0 0 rrlurlur 111221355 1 z1
0 0 rrlurduu 111221355 1 z1
0 0 rrlulrur 111221355 1 z1
0 0 rrullrru 111221355 1 z1
0 0 rrullrur 111221355 1 z1
0 0 rrullurr 111221355 1 z1
```

The first line gives the number of columns, nc, and
rows, nr, in that order. The next nr lines indicate how

notes or chords are assigned to nodes in the lattice. The notes are specified in abc notation, and are separated by spaces, not commas. It's important to keep this in mind because commas are used to denote octaves in abc notation. The lines are numbered starting at 0 at the top and going down to $nr - 1$, and the notes going left to right start at 0 and go to $nc - 1$. So in the above example, the chord $[CAF]$ is assigned to node $(0, 0)$ in the lattice, and the note B is assigned to the node $(2, 2)$. Be aware that this is upside down with respect to the way the lattice is drawn (see figure 21).

The remaining lines all have the same format. The first two numbers are the column and row number, respectively, of the starting node. Next, is the path string. Each character in the path string represents the direction to go from the current node. The letters l, r, u, and d indicate left, right, up, and down, respectively for a square lattice. For a triangular lattice, there are two additional letters, v, which indicates up and to the right, and e, which indicates down and to the left.

After the path string is the rhythm string, which is 1 character longer than the path string because the first character is used for the starting point. Next, is the number of times to repeat the path. The last item is a note or chord that is added to the end. In the case of the example above, it's a quarter note rest.

The MIDI file for this 3x3 example can be found on

the book's website. The MIDI file was generated by the following commands:

```
lat2abc 33 C 180 3x3.lat > 3x3.abc
abc2midi 3x3.abc
```

Note that there are many degrees of freedom for composing with a lat file. You can:

- use programs fsquare and ftri with different lattice sizes and start/end points to make different lattice paths.

- vary key mappings, including using stringed instruments.

- use images that map to a square or triangular grid to generate path strings.

- compose songs by using poetry to make rhythm strings.

- vary rhythm strings in other ways.

- vary repeats.

The number of walks between two points in a lattice will be a function of not just the length of the walk but also of the points. For the 3x3 lattice, we found that there were 504 walks of length 8 from node $(0, 0)$ to node $(2, 2)$, i.e. going diagonally across the lattice.

Even for such a small lattice, the number of walks increases very rapidly with the length of the walk. Below, we list the number of walks between different nodes in the lattice.

Number of walks from (0,0) to (0,0) is given by:
$a(n) = 8^{n/2-1} + 2^{n/2-1}$, $n = 2, 4, 6, \ldots$

n	0	2	4	6	8	10	12	14	16
$a(n)$	1	2	10	68	520	4112	32800	262208	2097280

Number of walks from (0,0) to (1,0) is given by:
$a(n) = (8^{(n-1)/2} + 2^{(n-1)/2})/2$, $n = 1, 3, 5, \ldots$

n	1	3	5	7	9	11	13	15
$a(n)$	1	5	34	260	2056	16400	131104	1048640

Number of walks from (0,0) to (2,0) is given by:
$a(n) = 8^{n/2-1}$, $n = 2, 4, 6, \ldots$

n	2	4	6	8	10	12	14	16
$a(n)$	1	8	64	512	4096	32768	262144	2097152

Number of walks from (0,0) to (1,1) is given by:
$a(n) = 2 * 8^{n/2-1}$, $n = 2, 4, 6, \ldots$

n	2	4	6	8	10	12	14	16
$a(n)$	2	16	128	1024	8192	65536	524288	4194304

Number of walks from (0,0) to (1,2) is given by:
$$a(n) = (8^{(n-1)/2} - 2^{(n-1)/2})/2, \ n = 3, 5, 7, \ldots$$

n	3	5	7	9	11	13	15
$a(n)$	3	30	252	2040	16368	131040	1048512

Number of walks from (0,0) to (2,2) is given by:
$$a(n) = 8^{n/2-1} - 2^{n/2-1}, \ n = 4, 6, 8, \ldots$$

n	4	6	8	10	12	14	16
$a(n)$	6	60	504	4080	32736	262080	2097024

Number of walks from (1,0) to (1,0) is given by:
$$a(n) = 8^{n/2}/4 + 2^{n/2-1}, \ n = 2, 4, 6, \ldots$$

n	0	2	4	6	8	10	12	14
$a(n)$	1	3	18	132	1032	8208	65568	524352

Number of walks from (1,0) to (1,1) is given by:
$$a(n) = 8^{(n-1)/2}, \ n = 1, 3, 5, \ldots$$

88

n	1	3	5	7	9	11	13	15
$a(n)$	1	8	64	512	4096	32768	262144	2097152

Number of walks from (1,0) to (2,1) is given by:
$a(n) = 2*8^{n/2-1}$, $n = 2, 4, 6, \ldots$

n	2	4	6	8	10	12	14	16
$a(n)$	2	16	128	1024	8192	65536	524288	4194304

Number of walks from (1,1) to (1,1) is given by:
$a(n) = 8^{n/2}/2$, $n = 2, 4, 6, \ldots$

n	0	2	4	6	8	10	12	14
$a(n)$	1	4	32	256	2048	16384	131072	1048576

There are ways to calculate the number of walks between points in a given lattice but they can be fairly complex. To find the number of walks, you can just run the **fsquare** or **ftri** program and count the number of lines it produces using program **wc**, as mentioned in the automata chapter. But be aware that for long walks, the number can easily be in the millions if not billions.

Bass Guitar

Now let's do an example where we look at the fret board of a bass guitar as a square lattice. The typical bass guitar has 4 strings which are represented as 4 rows in a square lattice. We can choose any number of frets to walk on, but for this example we'll confine ourselves to the first 4 frets, plus the open string. This means we need 5 columns in the square lattice, with the leftmost column being the open string, followed by frets 1 through 4.

The number of walks $a(n)$ on such a 4x5 square lattice from one corner to the diagonally opposite corner is shown in the table below as a function of the walk length n.

n	7	9	11	13	15	17
$a(n)$	35	714	10329	131560	1580150	18419194

Note that there are no such walks of length less than 7. We create the 35 walks of length 7 using the `fsquare` program as follows

```
fsquare 5 4 0 0 4 3 7
```

The output is:

```
rrrruuu rurruur urrurur
```

```
rrruruu rururru urruurr
rrruuru rururur ururrru
rrruuur ruruurr ururrur
rrurruu ruurrru ururur
rruruuru ruurrur uruurrr
rruruur ruururr uurrrru
rruurru ruuurrr uurrrur
rruurur urrrruu uurrurr
rruuurr urrruru uururrr
rurrruu urrruur uuurrrr
rurruru urrurru
```

where each walk starts at the bottom left corner $(0, 0)$ and ends at the top right corner $(4, 3)$. We include those walks in the lat file bguitar01a.lat whose first few lines are shown below

```
5 4
E,,, F,,, ^F,,, G,,, ^G,,,
A,,, ^A,,, B,,, C,, ^C,,
D,, ^D,, E,, F,, ^F,,
G,, ^G,, A,, ^A,, B,,
0 0 rrrruuu 11221122 1 z1
0 0 rrruruu 11221122 1 z1
0 0 rrruuru 11221122 1 z1
0 0 rrruuur 11221122 1 z1
0 0 rrurruu 11221122 1 z1
0 0 rrururu 11221122 1 z1
```

where we add a rhythm (11221122) after each walk, and specify a repeat of 1, a quarter note rest (z1) at the end of each walk, and start each walk at (0, 0).

The note assignments of the bass guitar, corresponding to the 2nd through 5th lines of the lat file shown above are illustrated in figure 22 in abc notation for the 4x5 lattice used. Again, note that this is upside down with respect to the file listing.

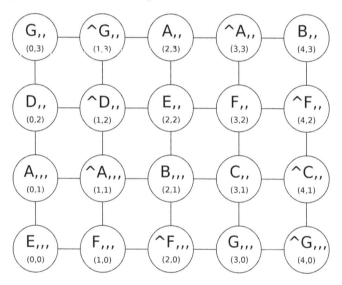

Figure 22: Bass guitar.

Using the above lat file, we create the MIDI file with commands:

```
lat2abc 34 C 180 bguitar01a.lat > bguitar01a.abc
abc2midi bguitar01a.abc -o bguitar01a.mid
```

The MIDI file for this bass guitar fret walk example can be found on the book's website.

Guitar

Since we just looked at a bass guitar, let's do a regular guitar. The typical guitar has 6 strings which are represented as 6 rows in a square lattice. Again, we can choose any number of frets to walk on, but we'll stick to the first 4 frets, plus the open string, for a total of 5 columns in the square lattice, with the leftmost column being the open string, followed by frets 1 through 4.

The number of walks $a(n)$ on such a 6x5 square lattice from one corner to the diagonally opposite corner is shown in the table below as a function of the walk length n.

n	9	11	13	15	17
$a(n)$	126	3498	64636	1008865	14436162

Note that there are no such walks of length less than 9. We create the 126 walks of length 9 using the `fsquare` program as follows

```
fsquare 5 6 0 0 4 5 9
```

The first few lines of output are:

```
rrrruuuuu
rrruruuuu
rrruuruuu
rrruuuruu
rrruuuuru
rrruuuuur
rrurruuuu
```

where each walk starts at the bottom left corner $(0,0)$ and ends at the top right corner $(4,5)$. We include those walks in the lat file guitar01.lat whose first few lines are shown below

```
5 6
E,, F,, ^F,, G,, ^G,,
A,, ^A,, B,, C, ^C,
D, ^D, E, F, ^F,
G, ^G, A, ^A, B,
B, C ^C D ^D
E F ^F G ^G
0 0 rrrruuuuu 1112211122 1 z4
0 0 rrruruuuu 1112211122 1 z4
0 0 rrruuruuu 1112211122 1 z4
0 0 rrruuuruu 1112211122 1 z4
0 0 rrruuuuru 1112211122 1 z4
0 0 rrruuuuur 1112211122 1 z4
```

where we use the rhythm (1112211122) after each walk, and as before, specify a repeat of 1, a whole note rest

(z4) at the end of each walk, and start each walk at
$(0,0)$.

The note assignments of the guitar, corresponding to
the 2nd through 7th lines of the lat file shown above
are illustrated in figure 23 in abc notation for the 6x5
lattice used. Again, note that this is upside down with
respect to the file listing.

Using the above lat file, we create the MIDI file with
commands:

```
lat2abc 25 C 180 guitar01.lat > guitar01.abc
abc2midi guitar01.abc -o guitar01.mid
```

The MIDI file for this guitar fret walk example can be
found and listened to on the book's website.

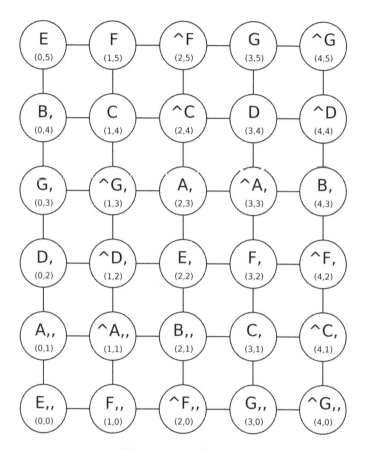

Figure 23: Guitar.

Accordion Buttons

As a last example, let's look at the bass side buttons on the accordion, specifically the Stradella bass system.

Our old German accordion, circa 1960, that Stefan learned to play on, has a buttonboard of 6 rows by 8 columns. So we'll use a square lattice of that size to walk on.

The note assignments of the Stradella bass system are illustrated in figure 24 in abc notation for the 6x8 lattice used. Again, note that this is upside down with respect to a lat file.

The number of walks $a(n)$ on such a 6x8 square lattice from one corner, $(0,0)$, to the diagonally opposite corner, $(7,5)$, is shown in the table below as a function of the walk length n.

n	12	14	16	18
$a(n)$	792	31174	766272	15202148

Note that there are no such walks of length less than 12. Similarly, the number of walks $a(n)$ on such a 6x8 square lattice from $(0,0)$ to $(7,0)$ is shown in the table below as a function of the walk length n.

n	7	9	11	13	15	17
$a(n)$	1	43	1079	21385	373660	6062064

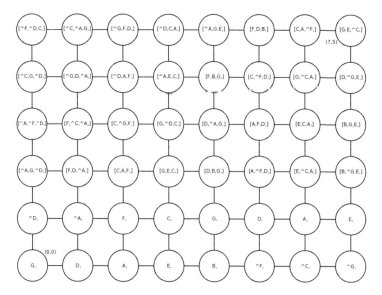

Figure 24: Accordion buttonboard.

Note that there are no such walks of length less than 7.

Let's sample 100 walks from the over 6 million walks of length 17 that start at $(0,0)$ and end at $(7,0)$ with the command

`fsquare 8 6 0 0 7 0 17 | ssline 6062064 100`

The first few output lines are:

```
rrrrrruduuulddrdr
rrrrrlrudlurdrrlr
rrrrrllrrrludrr
rrrrrlludrudrrlrr
rrrrruurudlrdlrrd
rrrrudurrludrrudd
rrrlrurrludrlrrrd
```

As before, with those walks we make a lat file `accbutton01.lat` whose first few lines are shown below:

```
8 6
G, D, A, E, B, ^F, ^C, ^G,
^D, ^A, F, C, G, D, A, E,
[^A,G,^D,] [F,D,^A,] [C,A,F,] [G,E,C,] [D,B,G,] [A,^F,D,] [E,^C,A,] [B,^G,E,]
[^A,^F,^D,] [F,^C,^A,] [C,^G,F,] [G,^D,C,] [D,^A,G,] [A,F,D,] [E,C,A,] [B,G,E,]
[^C,G,^D,] [^G,D,^A,] [^D,A,F,] [^A,E,C,] [F,B,G,] [C,^F,D,] [G,^C,A,] [D,^G,E,]
[^F,^D,C,] [^C,^A,G,] [^G,F,D,] [^D,C,A,] [^A,G,E,] [F,D,B,] [C,A,^F,] [G,E,^C,]
0 0 rrrrrruduuulddrdr 111221355111221355 1 z1
0 0 rrrrrlrudlurdrrlr 111221355111221355 1 z1
0 0 rrrrrllrrrlududrr 111221355111221355 1 z1
0 0 rrrrrlludrudrrlrr 111221355111221355 1 z1
0 0 rrrrruurudlrdlrrd 111221355111221355 1 z1
0 0 rrrrudurrludrrudd 111221355111221355 1 z1
0 0 rrrlrurrludrlrrrd 111221355111221355 1 z1
```

where we use the rhythm (111221355111221355) after each walk, and as before, specify a repeat of 1, a quarter note rest (z1) at the end of each walk, and start each walk at $(0, 0)$.

Using the above lat file, we create the MIDI file with commands:

```
lat2abc 25 C 180 accbutton01.lat > accbutton01.abc
abc2midi accbutton01.abc -o accbutton01.mid
```

Here we are using the "steel string acoustic guitar" program number (25 for timidity) instead of the accordion program number (21), simply because we like the sound better. The MIDI file for this accordion button walk example can be found on the book's website.

These are just a few simple examples of what you can do with lattice walks. You can draw your own lattice walks that trace out particular patterns and then turn those patterns into a melody. There are also two additional programs called **fsquares** and **fsquares2** that can be used to generate square lattice walks. **fsquares** allows a walk to stop for a given number of steps at any point so that a note or chord can repeat. **fsquare2** does not allow a walk to retrace its previous step so that **r** and **l** or **u** and **d** cannot immediately follow each other. These programs are described in the software chapter.

DE BRUIJN SEQUENCES

In our book on creating rhythms we used something called a de Bruijn sequence to create a very rich set of complex rhythms. These sequences can be used equally well to create melodies. We'll start with a short description of the theory behind them which is helpful in understanding why they produce interesting melodies.

First we look at binary de Bruijn sequences. A binary sequence is a string of symbols from an alphabet of two symbols. We use the numbers 0 and 1 as our two symbols. The number of binary sequences of length n is 2^n, since there are two choices for each term in the sequence, and there are n choices to be made. For $n = 3$ there are 8 possible sequences. They are: 000, 001, 010, 011, 100, 101, 110, 111.

The question is, can you construct a single binary sequence of length 8 that has all 8 of these sequences of length 3 as subsequences? It turns out that you can, it is called a de Bruijn sequence. The sequence is 11101000. Starting at the first term, and taking the next two terms gives you 111. Starting at the second term, and taking the next two terms gives you 110. Continuing on like this gives you 101, 010, 100, and 000. At this point, you treat the string as though it wraps around to the beginning, which then gives you the last two substrings 001 and 011.

What we just looked at is a binary de Bruijn sequence of order 3. It turns out there are de Bruijn sequences of all orders. Let $B(n)$ represent a de Bruijn sequence of order n. If you treat $B(n)$ as a circular sequence, where the end wraps around to the beginning, then it will contain all possible binary sequences of length n as subsequences. There are 2^n such sequences, therefore $B(n)$ must have length 2^n.

For $n > 2$, more than one unique $B(n)$ sequence exists. By unique, we mean that one sequence is not simply a circular shift of another. For $n = 1$, the only sequence is $B(1) = 10$. For $n = 2$, the only sequence is $B(2) = 1100$. For $n = 3$, there are two sequences: 11101000 and 11100010. In general, there are $2^{2^{n-1}-n}$ unique $B(n)$ sequences. Table 12 shows the number of $B(n)$ sequences for $n = 1$ to 7 and the length of each sequence.

n	length	number of sequences
1	2	1
2	4	1
3	8	2
4	16	16
5	32	2048
6	64	67108864
7	128	144115188075855872

Table 12: Number and length of $B(n)$ sequences.

The 16 unique $B(4)$ sequences are shown in table 13,

along with 16 of the 2048 $B(5)$ sequences.

$B(4)$	$B(5)$
1111010110010000	01111101011011001010011000 10000
1101011110010000	01110011111011000110101001000001
1111011001010000	01101111101011000111001010000010
1101111001010000	01110011111010010101100000100011
1011110011010000	01111101011011001010011000 00100
1111001011010000	01110011111011000110100000100101
1011001111010000	01011111011010100111000001000110
1100101111010000	01011011111000001000110010100111
1011110100110000	00111110101101110010100110001000
1111010010110000	00011111010110111001100000101001
1001111010110000	00111110101101110011000001001010
1010011110110000	00111111011100000100011010 0101011
1011010011110000	00010111001111101101010010001100
1101001011110000	00000100111110111001010110001101
1001101011110000	00001000110111110101100101001110
1010011011110000	00000100011001010011101011011111

Table 13: The 16 unique $B(4)$ sequences and 16 of the 2048 $B(5)$ sequences.

The program **kdebruijn** can be used to generate de Bruijn sequences for any order and any number of symbols, not just binary. The program and its use is described in the software chapter. For example, on the bash[14] command line in Linux, you can generate the $B(6)$ sequences in table 14 using the command:

---

[14]Bash is the default shell in most Linux distros and macOS. In Windows you can get the bash shell by installing *Cygwin* at https://www.cygwin.com/.

$B(6)$
011111101010111011011110010010110011010011000101000110000100000
011110011111101101110001110100110101011000011001001010001000001
011101101111110101011100011110010110011000011010001010010000010
011100011101010111100111111011001011010001010010011000001000011
011011101010111001111110110010110100100110000111000101000000100
011011110011111101100001100100101110001110100110101000001000101
011011101010111111011010011100011110010010100010110000001000110
011011110011111101001001101010110010111000000100001100010100011
011111101010111011011110010010110011010011000101000110000001000
010111100111111011011100011101001101010001011000011001000001001
010111100111111011011100011101010110010011000011010000000100101
010101110011111101110001110100110110000000100001100100101000101
010111100111111011011101001101010110010010100011100000010000110
010110111100111111011001011100011101000000100010100100110000110
010010111111011011101010110011010011110000001000011000101000111
010101110110111110000000100001100010100011100100101100110100111
001111110101011101101111001001011001101001110001010001100010000
001110110111111010101110001110010110011000011010010000001010001
001101110101011100111111011001011010011000011100010100000010010
001110110111111010101110001110010110010010100011100010100010010
001101101111111010101110001011010010110011011000110000011000011
001111110101011101101111001001011001101001110001010001100010100
001011110011111101101110001101011001001100001101000000100010101
001111110101011101101111001101001110000001000011001001010001101
001111110101011100000001000011000101000111010010011010101100010
000101110011111101101110001110100110101011001001010001000011000
000000100111011011111101010110001111001101001010001011000011001
000001000111111010101111011011110010110011100010100100110000110
000111111010101110111100111000000100001100100101000101101001101
000010011111101010111011011110010011001101000010001000010001100
000000100010010010011111101101011101011100011001010010110001110
000000100001100010100011100100101100110100111101010110110111111

Table 14: 32 of the $67,108,864$ $B(6)$ sequences.

```
for n in {0..31}; do kdebruijn 2 6 $n; done
```

There are many ways you can turn de Bruijn sequences into melodies. The simplest way is to assign a note or chord to each symbol in the sequence. For a binary sequence there are only two symbols. We used the first four sequences in table 14 to create the file dbbin1.str. The file is too big to show here, but you can view it on the book's website. The symbol 0 is assigned the chord [CEG], and 1 is assigned [FAC]. For the rhythm we used the same sequence as the note sequence, but with 0 replaced with 2. You can hear the result in the file dbbin1.mid on the book's website. We call this piece the "Ignatz Dance Song". The MIDI file was created with the following commands:

```
str2abc dbbin1.str 24 C 180 1/8 > dbbin1.abc
abc2midi dbbin1.abc -o dbbin1.mid
```

For more interesting melodies, you probably want more notes, and luckily there are de Bruijn sequences for any number of symbols. In general, the number of de Bruijn sequences of order n with k symbols is given by:

$$N(k, n) = \frac{(k!)^{k^{n-1}}}{k^n}$$

Each of the sequences is k^n symbols long. The number $N(k, n)$ becomes astronomically large as k and n

increase. Table 15 shows the number of sequences for $n = 2$ and $k = 2 \ldots 9$.

k	$N(k, 2)$
2	1
3	24
4	20736
5	995328000
6	3869835264000000
7	168584512763068416000000
8	10914006636158615818170531840000000
9	1347045535994707610868455547603630686208000000000

Table 15: Number of second order de Bruijn sequences for 2 through 9 symbols.

Let's look at a second order example using 3 symbols, i.e. $n = 2$ and $k = 3$. Table 15 says there are 24 de Bruijn sequences of this type. They are:

```
001221102 001211022 001122102 001121022
001122021 001120221 002112201 002122011
002211201 002212011 002211012 002210112
201122100 220112100 201221100 220121100
120221100 122021100 102211200 110221200
102112200 110212200 210112200 211012200
```

We put the 24 sequences in the file dbtri1.str shown below:

Having Fun Song

Stefan and Richard Hollos
Abrazol Publishing
3
[CEG] [FAC] [GBD]
001221102 221121114 1
001211022 221121114 1
001122102 221121114 1
001121022 221121114 1
001122021 221121114 1
001120221 221121114 1
002112201 221121114 1
002122011 221121114 1
002211201 221121114 1
002212011 221121114 1
002211012 221121114 1
002210112 221121114 1
201122100 221121114 1
220112100 221121114 1
201221100 221121114 1
220121100 221121114 1
120221100 221121114 1
122021100 221121114 1
102211200 221121114 1
110221200 221121114 1
102112200 221121114 1
110212200 221121114 1
210112200 221121114 1
211012200 221121114 1

The same rhythm was used for each sequence. You can listen to this as dbtri1.mid on the book's website. We call this piece the "Having Fun Song". The MIDI file was created with the following commands:

```
str2abc dbtri1.str 24 C 180 1/8 > dbtri1.abc
abc2midi dbtri1.abc -o dbtri1.mid
```

As a final example, we'll look at a third order de Bruijn sequence on 7 symbols. This has a length of $7^3 = 343$. There are an astronomical number of these sequences (10^{179}). We will use the one generated by the command:

```
kdebruijn 7 3 0
```

The sequence is:

```
0111222333444555666066166266366466560060160260360460560106
1161261361461562062162262362462562630631632633634635640641 6
4264364464565065165265365465505515525535545005015025035 04
5105115125135145205215225235245305315325335345405415425 43
5440441442443400401402403410411412413420421422423430431 43
2433033133230030130231031131232032132202212002012102110100
```

Note that we've broken it up into 6 lines here for viewability, but it's really one continuous string as you can see in the corresponding .str file, dbsept1.str found on the book's website. We used the son clave rhythm (33424) for this melody. We call this piece "Progress". The MIDI file (dbsept1.mid) was created with commands:

```
str2abc dbsept1.str 24 C 240 1/8 > dbsept1.abc
abc2midi dbsept1.abc -o dbsept1.mid
```

Note that the son clave rhythm has a length of 5, and
the note string length is 343, which is not divisible by
5. To make the melody not end abruptly with respect
to the rhythm, we add another two notes to make the
length 345. The natural choice for the two additional
notes is to add the first two notes to the end. This is
because the de Bruijn sequence is defined as wrapping
around to the beginning, and because this is a third
order de Bruijn sequence, adding the first two characters to the end makes it complete. This is what we've
done in dbsept1.str.

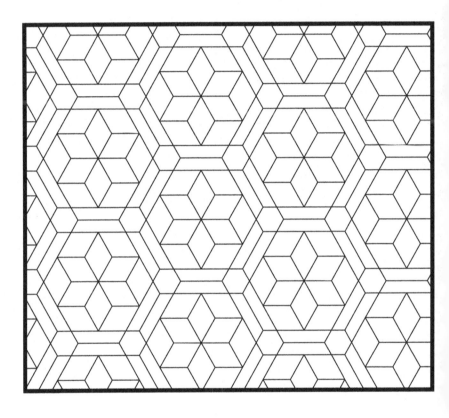

SOFTWARE

The software below can be found on this book's website:
http://www.abrazol.com/books/melody1/

The programs are written in the C programming language, and will have to be compiled before you can use them. You do not have to know C to use the programs or understand the contents of the book. There is a C language compiler for every major operating system. A good one that is also free is **gcc**, found at http://gcc.gnu.org/.

Programs

autogen2

> Generates all words of a given length accepted
> by an automaton. Result is printed to stdout.
>
> Usage: autogen2 file.aut2 n s e1 e2 ...
>   file.aut2 = automaton input file
>   n = length of words
>   s = start state
>   ei = end state i

fsquare

> Generates paths in a finite square lattice from
> (x,y) to (a,b). Result is printed to stdout.

111

```
Usage: fsquare nc nr x y a b n
  nc = number of columns
  nr = number of rows
  x = 0,1,...,nc-1
  y = 0,1,...,nr-1
  a = 0,1,...,nc-1
  b = 0,1,...,nr-1
  n = path length < 128
```

fsquare2

```
Generates paths in a finite square lattice from
(x,y) to (a,b). fsquare2 does not allow the
previous step to be retraced. Result is printed
to stdout.

Usage: fsquare2 nc nr x y a b n
  nc = number of columns
  nr = number of rows
  x = 0,1,...,nc-1
  y = 0,1,...,nr-1
  a = 0,1,...,nc-1
  b = 0,1,...,nr-1
  n = path length < 128
```

fsquares

```
Generates paths in a finite square lattice from
(x,y) to (a,b). Walk is allowed to stop at a
point for a number of steps. Result is printed
to stdout.

Usage: fsquares nc nr x y a b s n
  nc = number of columns
  nr = number of rows
  x = 0,1,...,nc-1
```

```
y = 0,1,...,nr-1
a = 0,1,...,nc-1
b = 0,1,...,nr-1
s = 0,1,... = number of stop steps allowed
n = path length < 128
```

ftri

Generates paths in a finite triangular lattice
from (x,y) to (a,b). Result is printed to stdout.

```
Usage: ftri nc nr x y a b n
    nc = number of columns
    nr = number of rows
    x = 0,1,...,nc-1
    y = 0,1,...,nr-1
    a = 0,1,...,nc-1
    b = 0,1,...,nr-1
    n = path length < 128
```

kdebruijn

Generates a de Bruijn sequence for k symbols of
order n. A different sequence is generated for
$v = 0$ to $k^{(n-1)}-1$.

```
Usage: kdebruijn k n v
    k = number of symbols used
    n = order of sequence (subsequence size)
    v = unique sequence parameter: 0 to k^(n-1)-1
```

lat2abc

Converts walks on a square or triangular lattice
to melodies in abc notation. Walks can be
generated by program fsquare, fsquare2, fsquares
or ftri. Input file specifies: lattice size, note

mapping, and any number of lines containing
starting point, walk, rhythm, repeats, and rest.
Result is printed to stdout.

Usage: lat2abc inst key tempo file.lat
    inst = MIDI instrument (program) number
    key   = musical key, e.g. C
    tempo = beats per minute, e.g. 180
    file.lat = name of lattice file

pautogen

Generates words of a given length accepted
by a probabilistic automaton. Result is printed
to stdout.

Usage: pautogen file.pat n s seed
    file.pat = probabilistic automaton file
    n = length of words
    s = start state
    seed = random number seed [0..4294967295]

ssline

Prints a random subset of the first n lines read
from stdin. The size of the subset is m. All
subsets of size m have the same probability.
Result is printed to stdout.

Usage: ssline n m
    n = number of lines to read from stdin
    m = subset size to sample

str2abc

Converts strings in a file into abc notation.
Result is printed to stdout.

```
Usage: str2abc file.str inst key tempo unit
   file.str = input file
   inst = MIDI instrument (program) number
   key = musical key, e.g. C
   tempo = beats per minute, e.g. 180
   unit = unit note length, e.g. 1/4 is a
      quarter note
```

Input File Formats

autogen2 automaton input file (.aut2)
   This input file defines an automaton as read by program
   autogen2.

```
FORMAT:
   ns
   0 (sn00,sym00) (sn01,sym01) ...
   1 (sn10,sym10) (sn11,sym11) ...
   ...

   ns = total number of states of automaton
      = number of lines to follow this one.
   Each additional line after the first defines a
   state, named consecutively starting from 0. A
   state is defined in terms of what states it can
   transition to and what symbol is output on that
   transition. There is a pair of parentheses for
   each transition a state can make. Inside each
   pair of parentheses is first a state number
   (snij), followed by a comma, then the symbol
   that is output on the transition (symij). The
   symbol can be any ascii string of 64 characters
```

116

or less, on the condition that the entire line
is no longer than 512 characters. The symbol
starts immediately after the comma and goes to
the character preceeding the closing parenthesis.
Any spaces in that region will be part of the
symbol.
EXAMPLE
For this automaton:

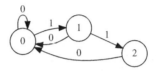

The .aut2 input file is:
3
0 (0,0) (1,1)
1 (0,0) (2,1)
2 (0,0)

lat2abc lattice input file (.lat)

This input file defines a square or triangular lattice as
read by program lat2abc. It also defines how the lattice
walks are translated to abc notation.

FORMAT:
```
nc nr
note(0,0) note(1,0) ... note(nc-1,0)
note(0,1) note(1,1) ... note(nc-1,1)
...
note(0,nr-1) note(1,nr-1) ... note(nc-1,nr-1)
sc1 sr1 pathString1 rhythmString1 repeat1 endnote1
```

```
sc2 sr2 pathString2 rhythmString2 repeat2 endnote2
...
```

The first line gives the number of columns, nc, and
rows, nr, in that order. The next nr lines indicate
how notes or chords are assigned to nodes in the
lattice. The notes are specified in abc notation,
and are separated by spaces, not commas. It's
important to keep this in mind because commas are
used to denote octaves in abc notation. The lines
are numbered starting at 0 at the top and going
down to nr-1, and the notes going left to right
start at 0 and go to nc-1. Be aware that this is
upside down with respect to the way the lattice
is drawn. See the example below.

The remaining lines all have the same format. The
first two numbers are the column and row number,
respectively, of the starting node. Next, is the
path string. Each character in the path string
represents the direction to go from the current
node. The letters l, r, u, and d indicate left,
right, up, and down, respectively for a square
lattice. For a triangular lattice, there are two
additional letters, v, which indicates up and to
the right, and e, which indicates down and to the
left. Lastly, the letter s indicates to stay where
we are for the current step.

After the path string is the rhythm string, which
is 1 character longer than the path string because
the first character is used for the starting point.
Next, is the number of times to repeat the path.
The last item is a note or chord that is added to
the end. In the case of the example below, it's a

quarter note rest.
EXAMPLE
    For this 3x3 square lattice:

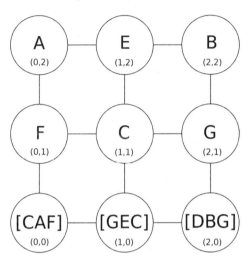

    A proper .lat input file is:
3 3
[CAF] [GEC] [DBG]
F C G
A E B
0 0 rrlrluru 111221355 1 z1
0 0 rrlurlur 111221355 1 z1
0 0 rrlurduu 111221355 1 z1
0 0 rrlulrur 111221355 1 z1
0 0 rrullrru 111221355 1 z1
0 0 rrullrur 111221355 1 z1
0 0 rrullurr 111221355 1 z1

pautogen probabilistic automaton input file (.pat)
    This input file defines a probabilistic automaton as read
    by program **pautogen**.

The pautogen input file format is the same as
that of autogen2, except for an additional
probability term inside the parentheses at
the end, separated by a comma. The
probabilities on each line should sum to 1.0.
EXAMPLE
For this automaton:

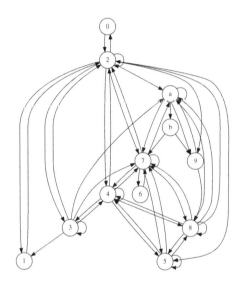

The .pat input file is:

```
12
0 (2,2,1.0)
1 (2,2,1.0)
2 (0,0,0.0625) (1,1,0.0625) (2,2,0.125) (3,3,0.3125) (4,4,0.1875)
  (5,5,0.0625) (7,7,0.0625) (9,9,0.0625) (10,a,0.0625)
3 (1,1,0.0625) (2,2,0.375) (3,3,0.1875) (4,4,0.25) (7,7,0.0625) (10,a,0.0625)
4 (2,2,0.125) (3,3,0.25) (4,4,0.3125) (5,5,0.125) (7,7,0.125) (8,8,0.0625)
5 (4,4,0.25) (5,5,0.1875) (7,7,0.375) (8,8,0.1875)
6 (7,7,1.0)
7 (2,2,0.0625) (4,4,0.3125) (5,5,0.0625) (6,6,0.0625) (7,7,0.25) (8,8,0.1875)
  (10,a,0.0625)
8 (2,2,0.0625) (4,4,0.0625) (5,5,0.0625) (7,7,0.5625) (8,8,0.125) (10,a,0.125)
9 (8,8,0.5) (10,a,0.5)
10 (7,7,0.25) (8,8,0.4375) (9,9,0.1875) (10,a,0.0625) (11,b,0.0625)
11 (7,7,0.375) (9,9,0.625)
```

Note that probability values are not indicated
in the automaton figure, and are presumed to
come from additional knowledge of the problem
at hand.

str2abc input file (.str)

This input file specifies the note/chord, melody, and repeat information that will be converted to abc notation
by program str2abc.

```
FORMAT:
    title (T: field in abc notation)
    composer (C: field in abc notation)
    transcriber (Z: field in abc notation)
    nn = number of notes or chords used
    note1 note2 ... noten
    noteString1 rhythmString1 repeats1
    noteString2 rhythmString2 repeats2
    ...
```

The first three lines of the file are just
documentation strings: the title, composer,
and transcriber fields defined by the abc
notation standard. The next line contains
a single integer indicating the number of
notes or chords listed on the following
line. Next, is the line with the notes or
chords in abc notation separated by spaces.
The rest of the lines each contain three
elements separated by a space: first the
note string, then the rhythm string, then
the number of repeats of that line. The
note string and rhythm string can each be
up to 128 characters long. The note string
cannot contain spaces, only digits 0
through 9, and lower case letters. The note

string is translated to notes/chords
according to the list of notes/chords
on the fifth line of the file. All 0's
in the note string are translated to the
first note/chord of the note/chord list.
All 1's are translated to the second
note/chord, and so on, so that all 9's are
translated to the tenth note/chord. If
there are lower case letters in the note
string, all a's are translated to the
eleventh note/chord, all b's are
translated to the twelfth note/chord,
and so on, so that all z's are translated
to the 3Gth note/chord. If there are fewer
notes/chords on the fifth line of the file
than is required by the digits and letters
of the note string, then the translation is
done modulo the number of notes/chords.
That is, if there are only three notes or
chords specified, then the digit 4 will
be translated to the second note/chord.
Similarly, the rhythm string cannot contain
spaces, only digits 0 through 9, and lower
case letters. The rhythm string is
translated to a rhythm according to the
unit note length specified in the last
input to the str2abc program. For example,
if the unit note length is specified as
1/4, then a 1 in the rhythm string is
translated to a quarter note, a 2 is
translated to a half note, a 3 is
translated to a dotted half note, a 4 is
translated to a whole note, and so on.
Following the rhythm string is the number
of repeats of that line, that is, how

many times the melody of the line is to
be repeated. It can be any positive
integer.

EXAMPLE
Fibo example 1
Stefan and Richard
Abrazol Publishing
2
[CEG] [FAC]
00100101010100000100010 121221111224 1
00101010100100101010 121221111224 1

NOTES AND CHORDS

Note	Rest	Length
‖O‖	▬	Double
O	▬	Whole
𝅗𝅥	▬	Half
𝅘𝅥	𝄾	Quarter
♪	𝄿	1/8
𝅘𝅥𝅯	𝅀	1/16
𝅘𝅥𝅰	𝅁	1/32

• Dot adds 50%

124

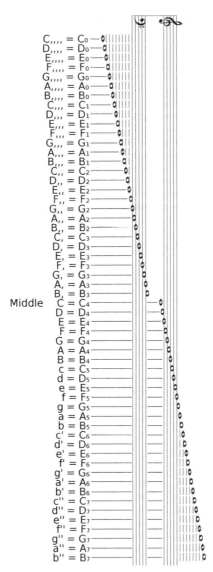

Musical notes in abc and scientific pitch notation.

Circle of Major Triads

This circle can be used to select three note chords.

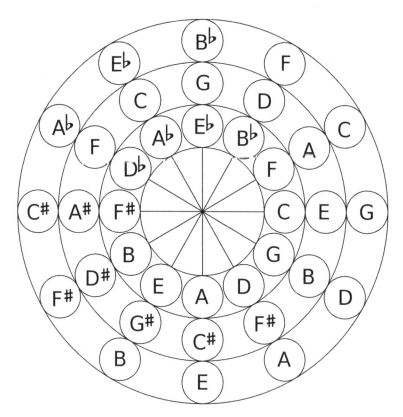

Octave Keys

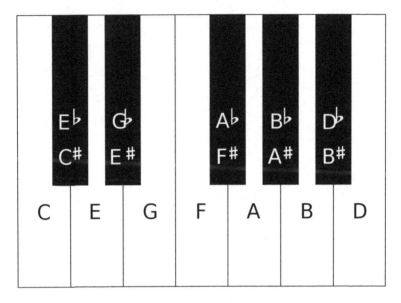

MIDI PROGRAM NUMBERS

This list differs slightly from the General MIDI program numbers[15], in that they start at 0 instead of 1. Some MIDI players start at 1 and some start at 0. The Timidity MIDI player starts at 0.

Piano
0 Acoustic Grand Piano
1 Bright Acoustic Piano
2 Electric Grand Piano
3 Honky-tonk Piano
4 Electric Piano
5 Electric Piano
6 Harpsichord
7 Clavinet

Chromatic Percussion
8 Celesta
9 Glockenspiel
10 Music Box
11 Vibraphone
12 Marimba
13 Xylophone
14 Tubular Bells
15 Dulcimer

Organ
16 Drawbar Organ
17 Percussive Organ
18 Rock Organ
19 Church Organ
20 Reed Organ
21 Accordion
22 Harmonica
23 Tango Accordion

Guitar
24 Acoustic Guitar (nylon)
25 Acoustic Guitar (steel)
26 Electric Guitar (jazz)
27 Electric Guitar (clean)
28 Electric Guitar (muted)
29 Overdriven Guitar
30 Distortion Guitar
31 Guitar Harmonics

Bass
32 Acoustic Bass

Strings
40 Violin

---

[15]The list is adapted from that on the Wikipedia page for **General MIDI** at https://en.wikipedia.org/wiki/General_MIDI

33 Electric Bass (finger)
34 Electric Bass (pick)
35 Fretless Bass
36 Slap Bass 1
37 Slap Bass 2
38 Synth Bass 1
39 Synth Bass 2

Ensemble
48 String Ensemble
49 String Ensemble
50 Synth Strings 1
51 Synth Strings 2
52 Choir Aahs
53 Voice Oohs
54 Synth Choir
55 Orchestra Hit

Reed
64 Soprano Sax
65 Alto Sax
66 Tenor Sax
67 Baritone Sax
68 Oboe
69 English Horn
70 Bassoon
71 Clarinet

Synth Lead
80 Lead 1 (square)
81 Lead 2 (sawtooth)
82 Lead 3 (calliope)
83 Lead 4 (chiff)
84 Lead 5 (charang)
85 Lead 6 (voice)

41 Viola
42 Cello
43 Contrabass
44 Tremolo Strings
45 Pizzicato Strings
46 Orchestral Harp
47 Timpani

Brass
56 Trumpet
57 Trombone
58 Tuba
59 Muted Trumpet
60 French Horn
61 Brass Section
62 Synth Brass 1
63 Synth Brass 2

Pipe
72 Piccolo
73 Flute
74 Recorder
75 Pan Flute
76 Blown bottle
77 Shakuhachi
78 Whistle
79 Ocarina

Synth Pad
88 Pad 1 (new age)
89 Pad 2 (warm)
90 Pad 3 (polysynth)
91 Pad 4 (choir)
92 Pad 5 (bowed)
93 Pad 6 (metallic)

86 Lead 7 (fifths)	94 Pad 7 (halo)
87 Lead 8 (bass+lead)	95 Pad 8 (sweep)

Synth Effects	Ethnic
96 FX 1 (rain)	104 Sitar
97 FX 2 (soundtrack)	105 Banjo
98 FX 3 (crystal)	106 Shamisen
99 FX 4 (atmosphere)	107 Koto
100 FX 5 (brightness)	108 Kalimba
101 FX 6 (goblins)	109 Bagpipe
102 FX 7 (echoes)	110 Fiddle
103 FX 8 (sci-fi)	111 Shanai

Percussivo	Sound Effects
112 Tinkle Bell	120 Guitar Fret Noise
113 Agogo	121 Breath Noise
114 Steel Drums	122 Seashore
115 Woodblock	123 Bird Tweet
116 Taiko Drum	124 Telephone Ring
117 Melodic Tom	125 Helicopter
118 Synth Drum	126 Applause
119 Reverse Cymbal	127 Gunshot

FURTHER READING

- *Creating Rhythms*, Hollos and Hollos, 2014

- *Finite Automata and Regular Expressions: Problems and Solutions*, Hollos and Hollos, 2013

- *Music, Physics and Engineering*, Second Edition, Harry F. Olson, 1967

- *Barron's AP Music Theory*, Nancy Scoggin, 2010

- *Melody Wikipedia page*

- *General MIDI Wikipedia page*

- *Casio Song Book*, 07HCOSCOREWL1B

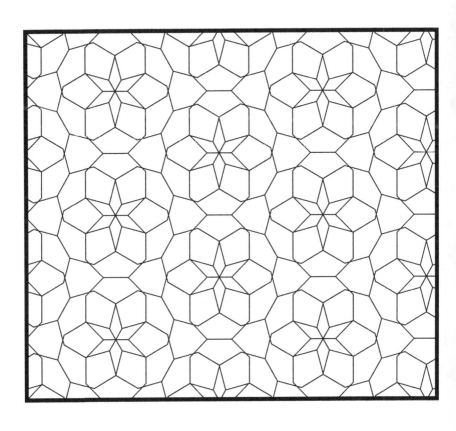

ACKNOWLEDGMENTS

In ordinary life we hardly realize that we receive a great deal more than we give, and that it is only with gratitude that life becomes rich. It is very easy to overestimate the importance of our own achievements in comparison with what we owe to others.

Dietrich Bonhoeffer, letter to parents from prison, Sept. 13, 1943

We'd like to thank our parents, Istvan and Anna Hollos, for helping us in many ways.

We thank the makers and maintainers of all the software we've used in the production of this book, including: gcc, the abcMIDI package, TiMidity++, Emacs text editor, LaTeX typesetting system, Inkscape, mupdf and evince document viewers, Maxima computer algebra system, bash shell, and the GNU/Linux operating system.

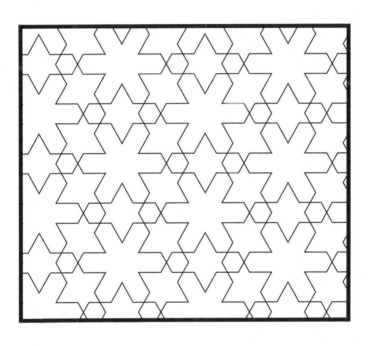

ABOUT THE AUTHORS

Stefan Hollos and **J. Richard Hollos** are physicists
by training. In addition to math and physics, they
enjoy creating music and visual art, and being in the
great outdoors. They are the authors of:

- **Hexagonal Tilings and Patterns**

- **Combinatorics II Problems and Solutions: Counting Patterns**

- **Information Theory: A Concise Introduction**

- **Recursive Digital Filters: A Concise Guide**

- **Art of Pi**

- **Creating Noise**

- **Art of the Golden Ratio**

- **Creating Rhythms**

- **Pattern Generation for Computational Art**

- **Finite Automata and Regular Expressions: Problems and Solutions**

- **Probability Problems and Solutions**

- Combinatorics Problems and Solutions

- The Coin Toss: Probabilities and Patterns

- Pairs Trading: A Bayesian Example

- Simple Trading Strategies That Work

- Bet Smart: The Kelly System for Gambling and Investing

- Signals from the Subatomic World: How to Build a Proton Precession Magnetometer

They are brothers and business partners at Exstrom Laboratories LLC in Longmont, Colorado. Their website is exstrom.com

THANK YOU

Thank you for buying this book.

Sign up for our newsletter (Abrazol Publishing) and get a 50% off coupon for any of our ebooks. The newsletter has information on new editions, new products, and special offers. Just go to

http://www.abrazol.com/

and enter your name and email address.

Made in the USA
Las Vegas, NV
08 August 2021